Rebus Puzzle Activities

Welcome to the exciting world of the rebus—where you **R**eason and **E**xamine **B**y **U**ncovering **S**ymbols! These picture puzzles challenge, educate, and entertain both children and adults by stimulating critical thinking skills. Solutions are attained through a combination of letter recognition, sound skills, vocabulary recollection, and prior exposure to common idioms, phrases, book titles, characters, and so on. When a person solves a rebus, it's almost possible to picture an illuminated light bulb with the word "Eureka" glowing brightly inside!

Note: If a letter is shown in shadow, ℝ for example, the alphabet letter name /ahr/ is denoted.

If a letter is shown in normal print, R for example, the most common sound for that letter /r/ is denoted.

Use in the classroom to . . .

1. combat morning sluggishness with a fun challenge during house-keeping procedures such as, taking attendance and lunch count and collecting money. Display a card daily or weekly in the front of the classroom. (You may want to laminate for durability.)

2. enhance learning/activity centers for students.

3. motivate students by having contests wherein teams are given the same rebuses to solve in a given time frame.

4. occasionally spice up a homework assignment.

5. provide opportunity for students to create original rebuses.

Use at home to . . .

1. encourage friendly, family competition on trips.

2. create your own party games with rebuses.

Wherever or however you choose to use our rebuses, we know that you will enjoy uncovering each clue! So put on your "thinking caps" and . . . begin!

Answer Key can be found at the back of the book.

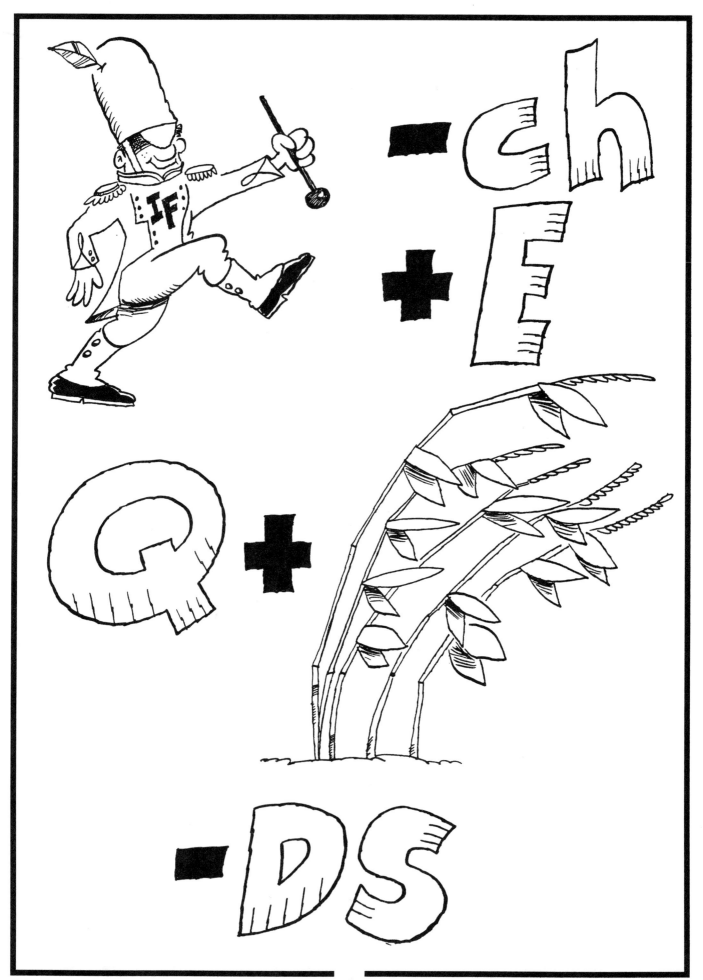

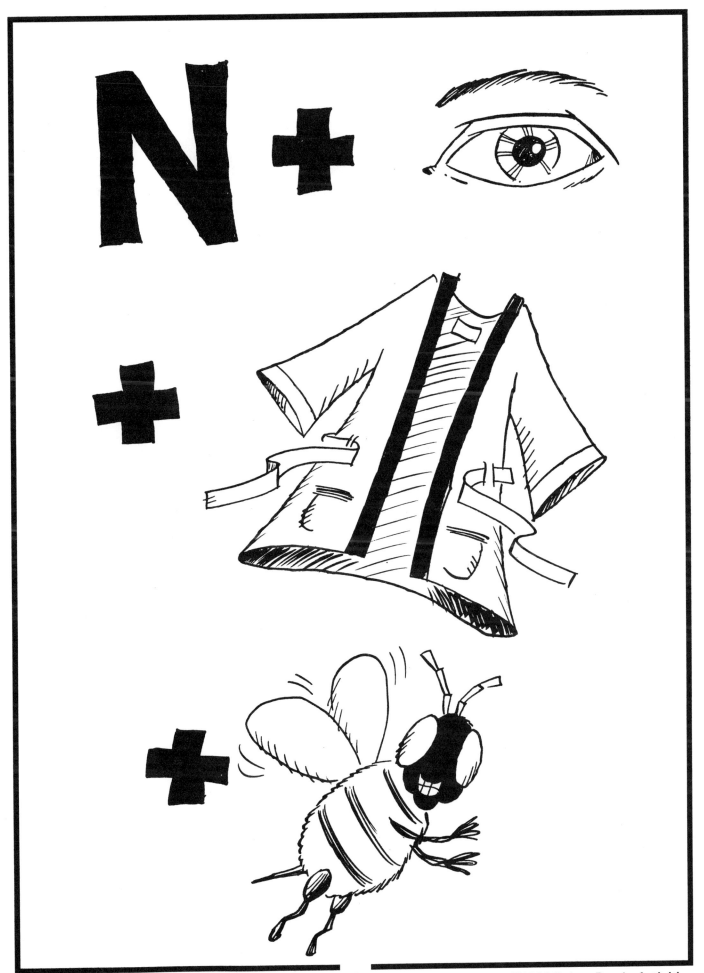

IF8363 Rebus Puzzle Activities

-skirt + COLA

10

IF8363 Rebus Puzzle Activities

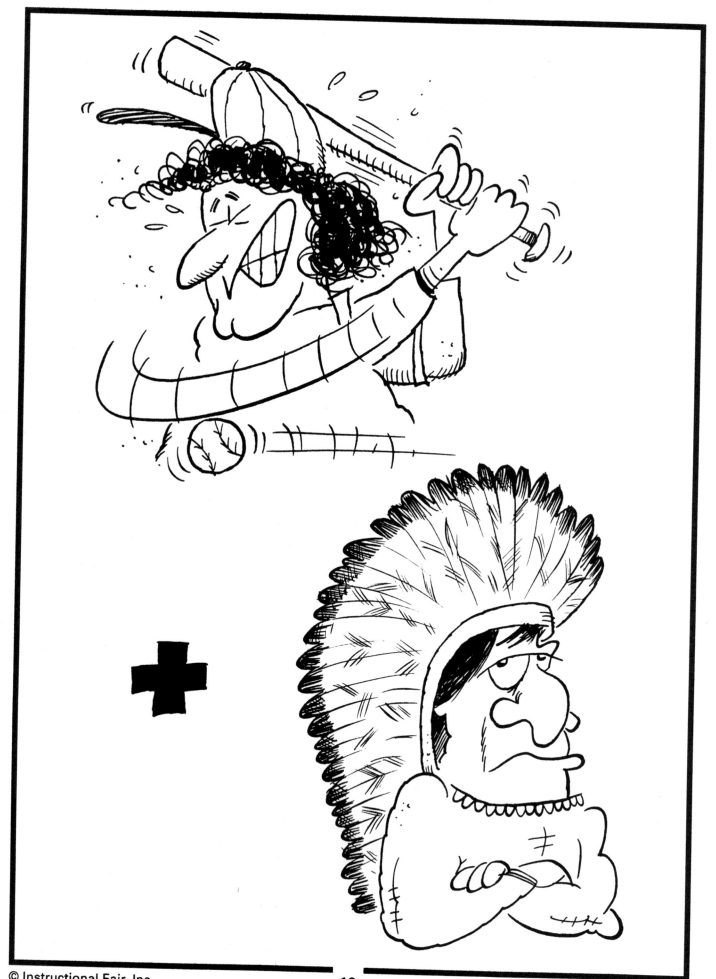

 IF8363 Rebus Puzzle Activities

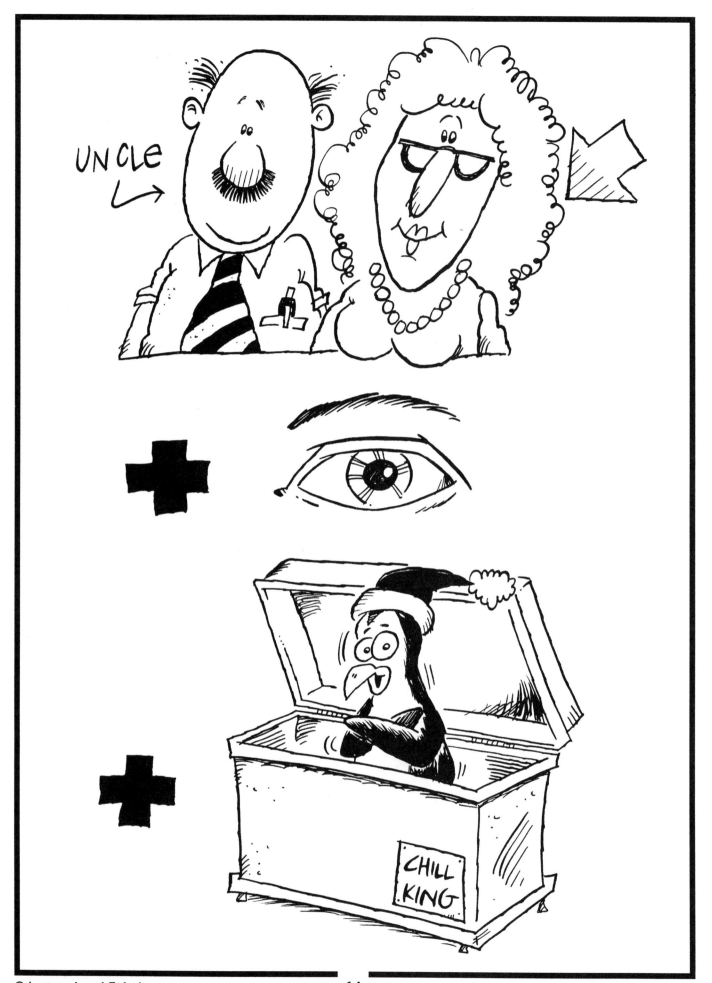

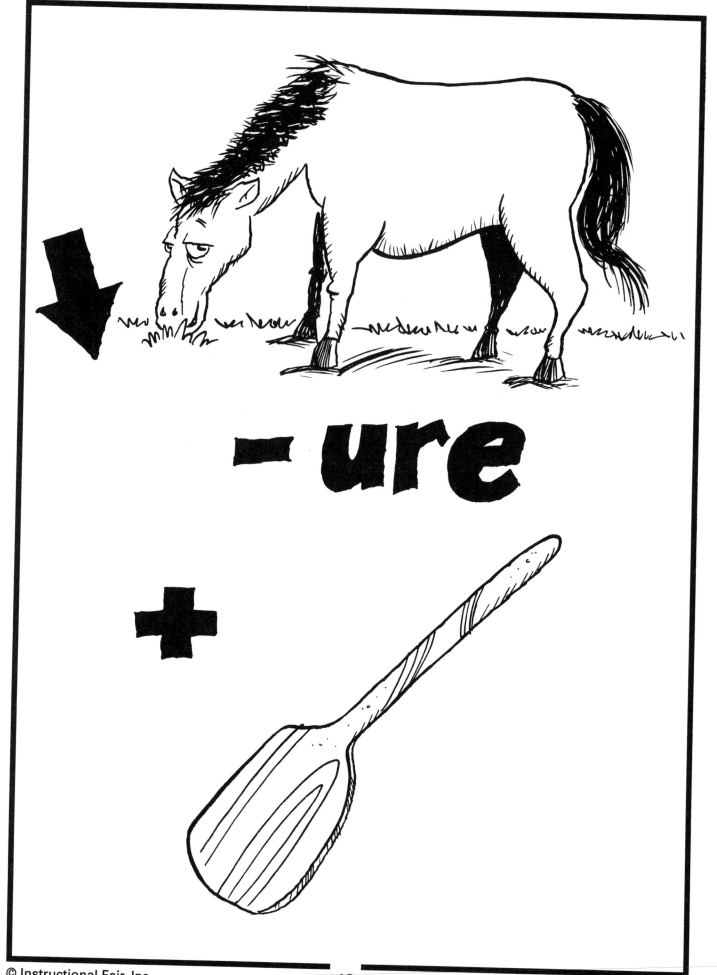

- ure

+

18

IF8363 Rebus Puzzle Activities

IF8363 Rebus Puzzle Activities

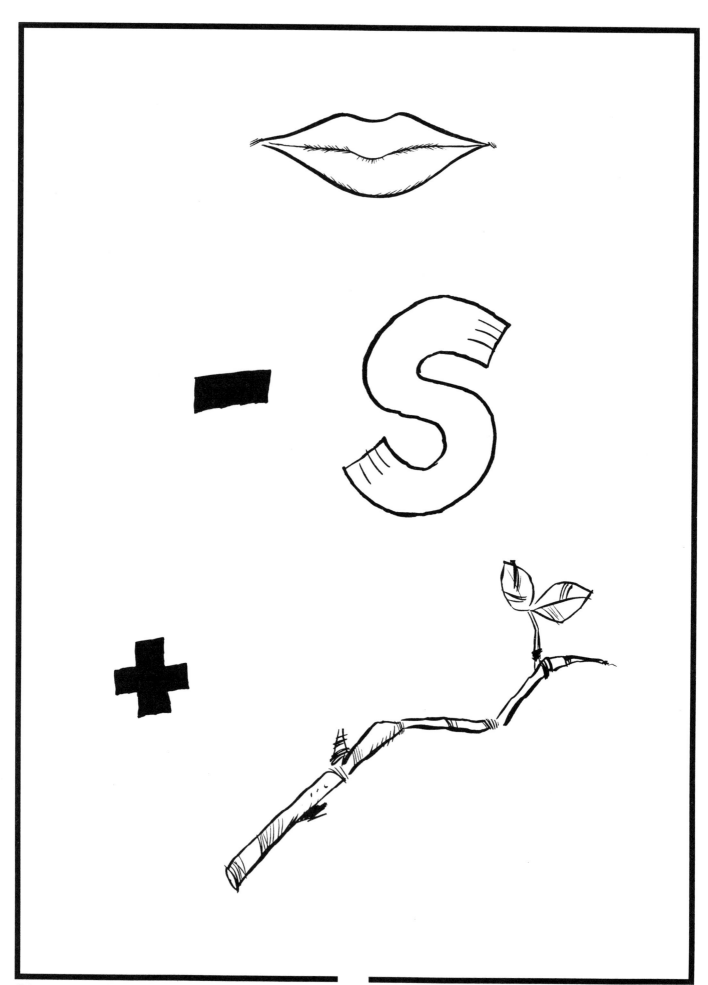

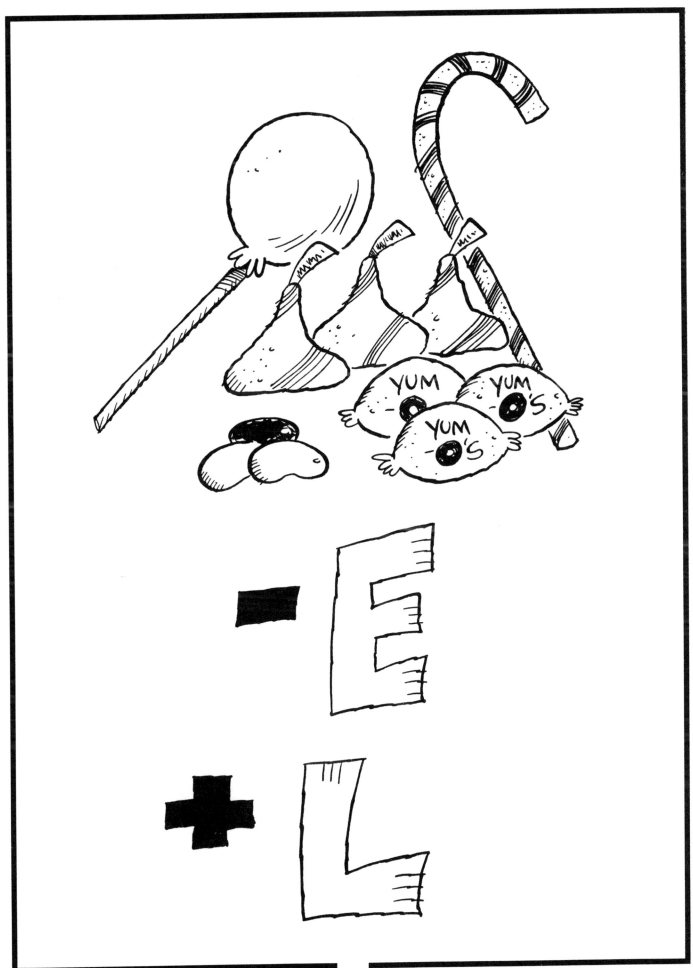

IF8363 Rebus Puzzle Activities

IF8363 Rebus Puzzle Activities

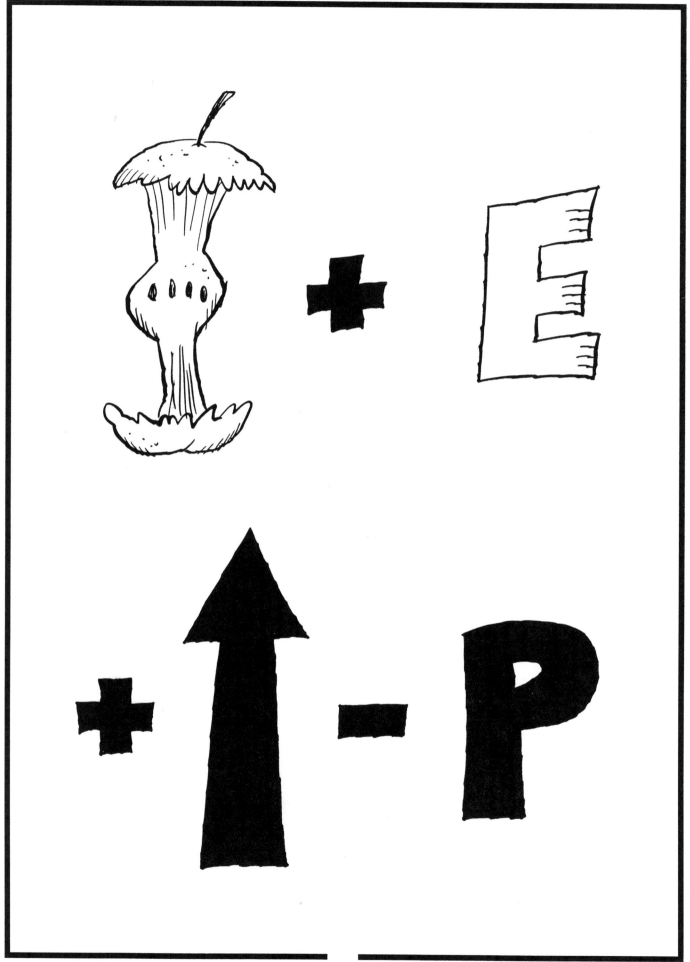

IF8363 Rebus Puzzle Activities

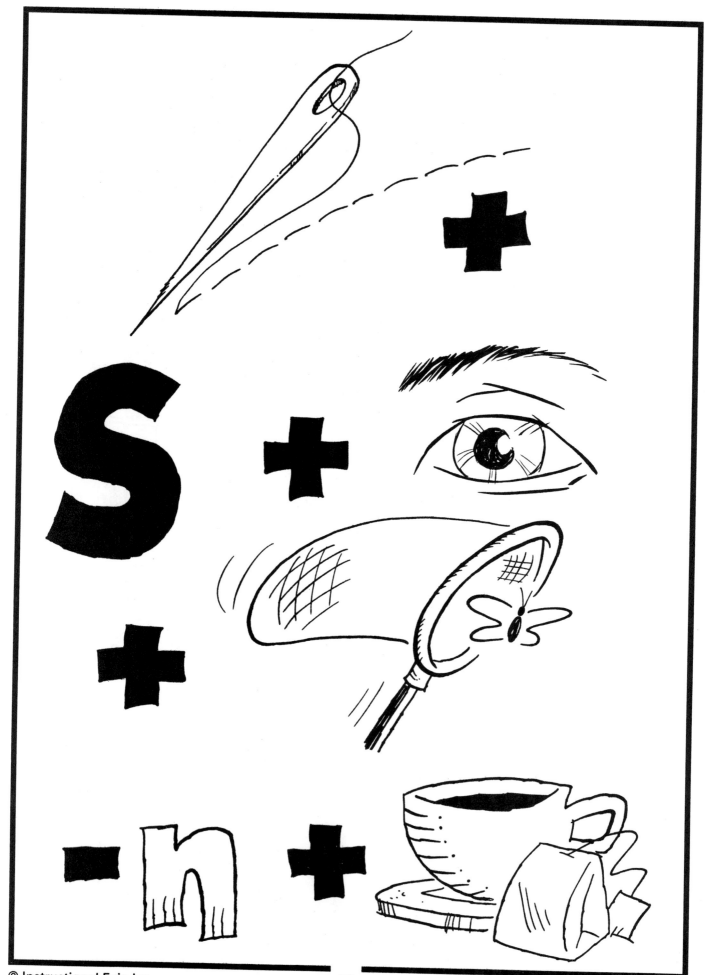

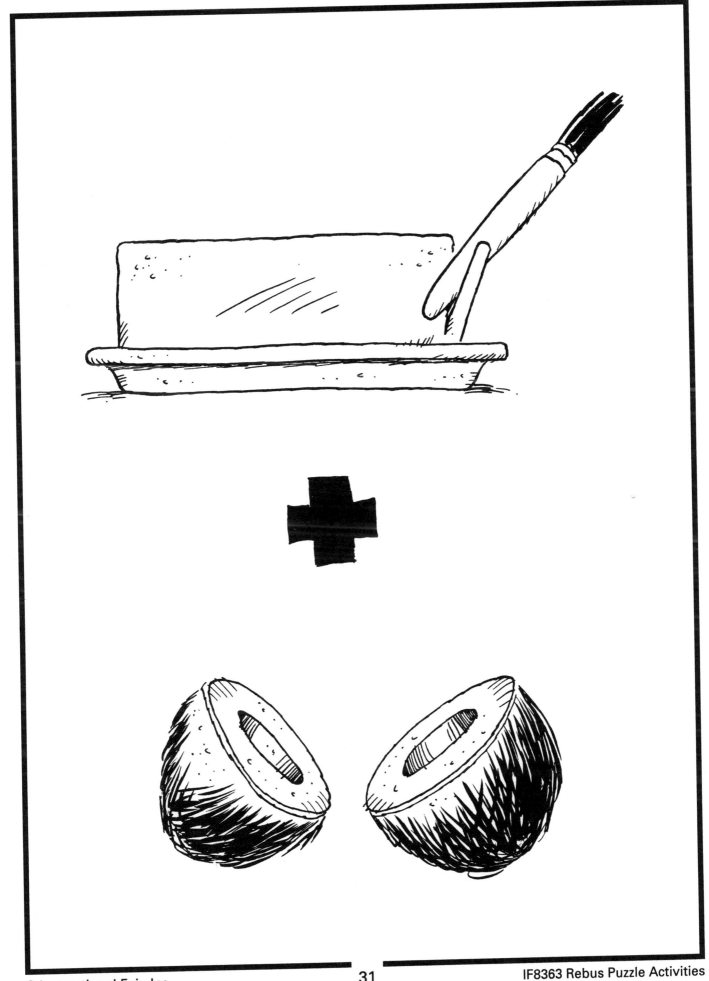

IF8363 Rebus Puzzle Activities

32

IF8363 Rebus Puzzle Activities

IF8363 Rebus Puzzle Activities

IF8363 Rebus Puzzle Activities

IF8363 Rebus Puzzle Activities

IF8363 Rebus Puzzle Activities

IF8363 Rebus Puzzle Activities

44

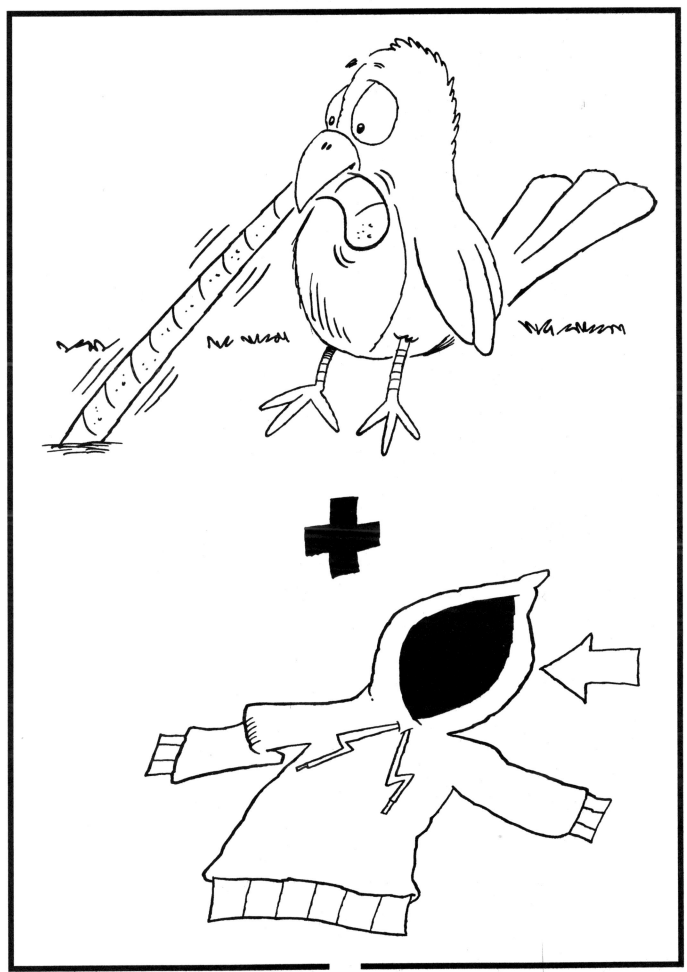

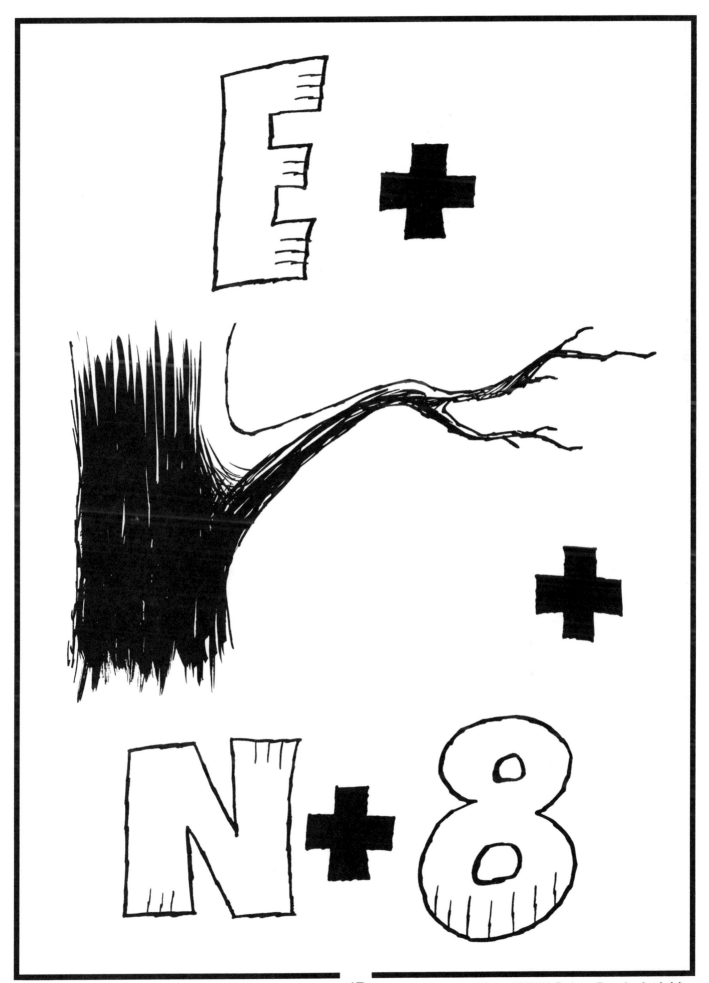

IF8363 Rebus Puzzle Activities

48

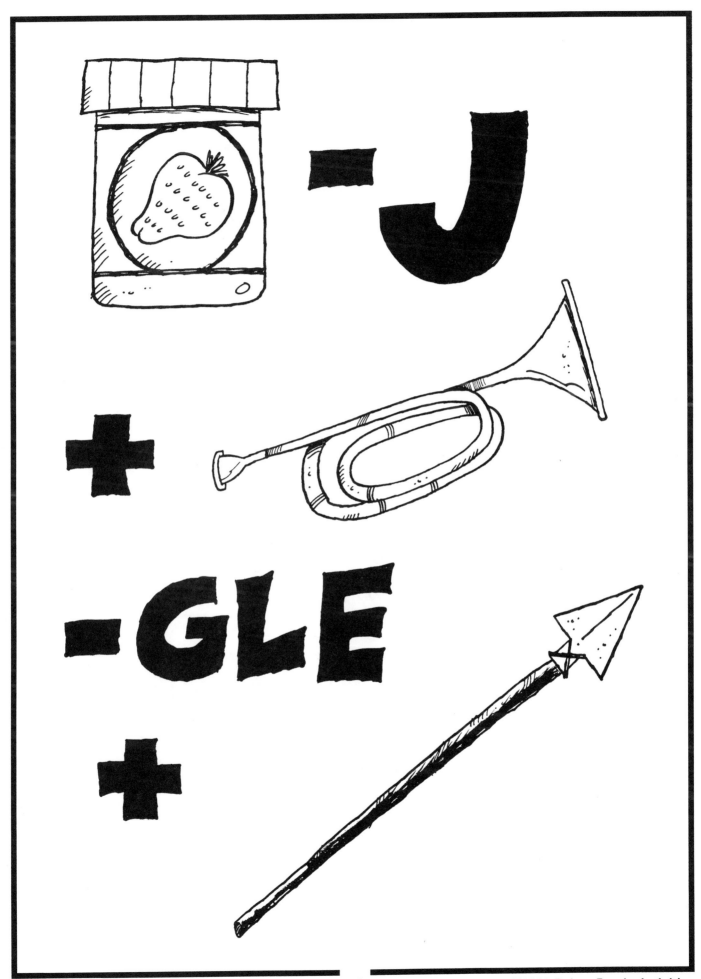

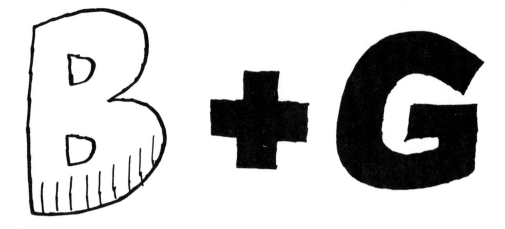

+

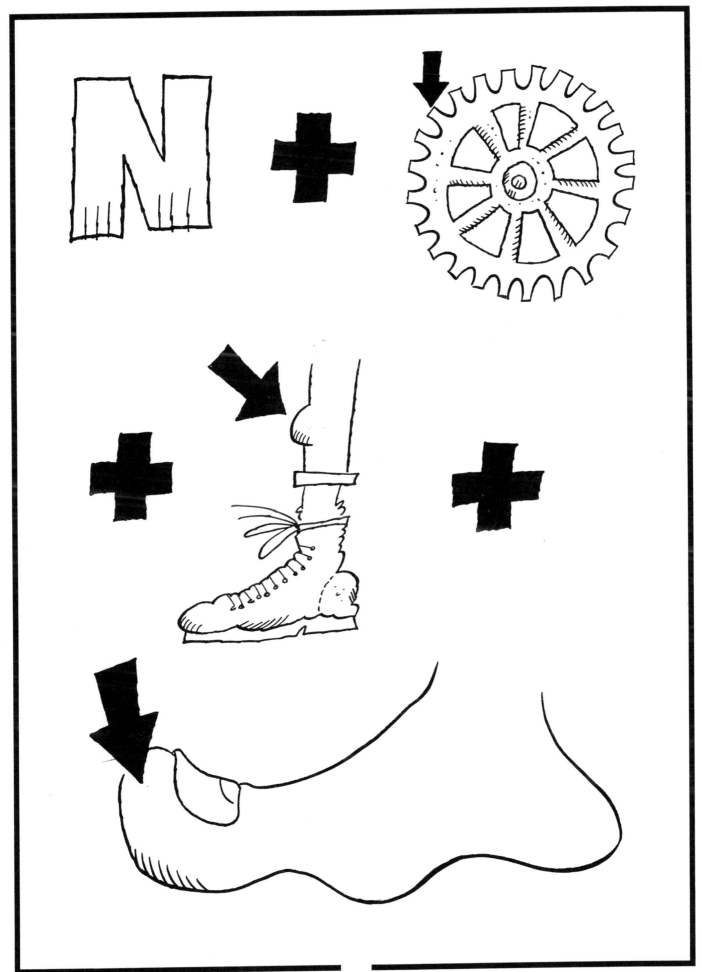

IF8363 Rebus Puzzle Activities

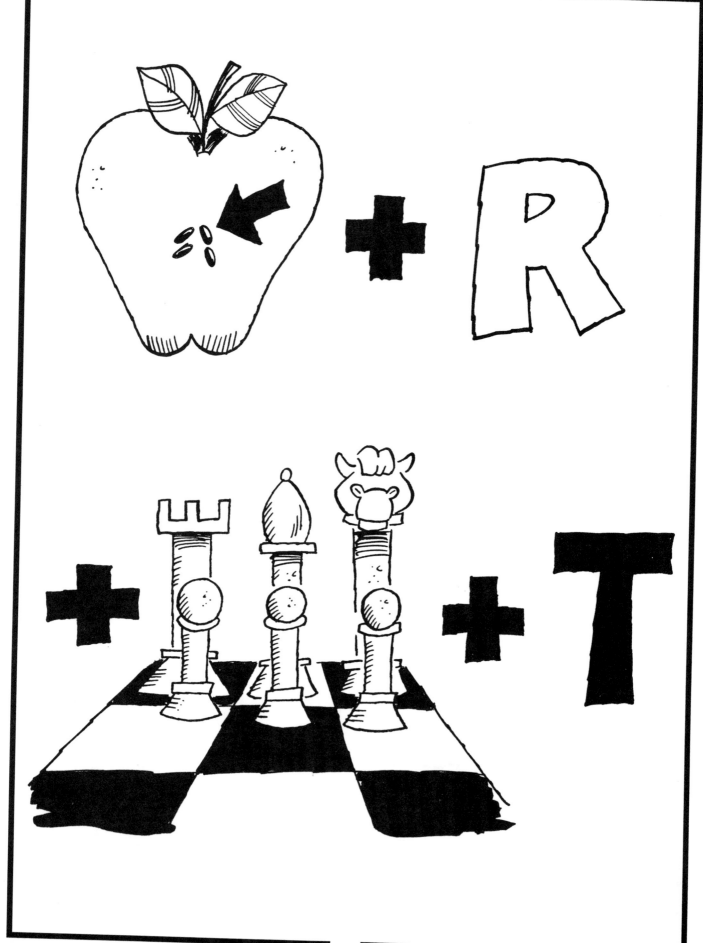

IF8363 Rebus Puzzle Activities

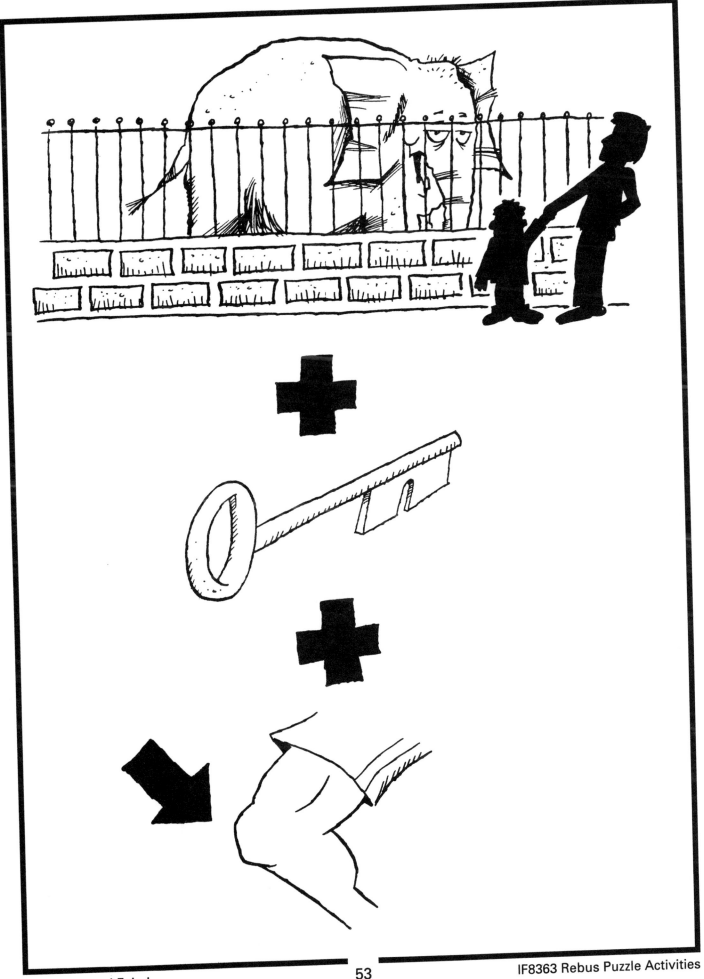

IF8363 Rebus Puzzle Activities

IF8363 Rebus Puzzle Activities

IF8363 Rebus Puzzle Activities

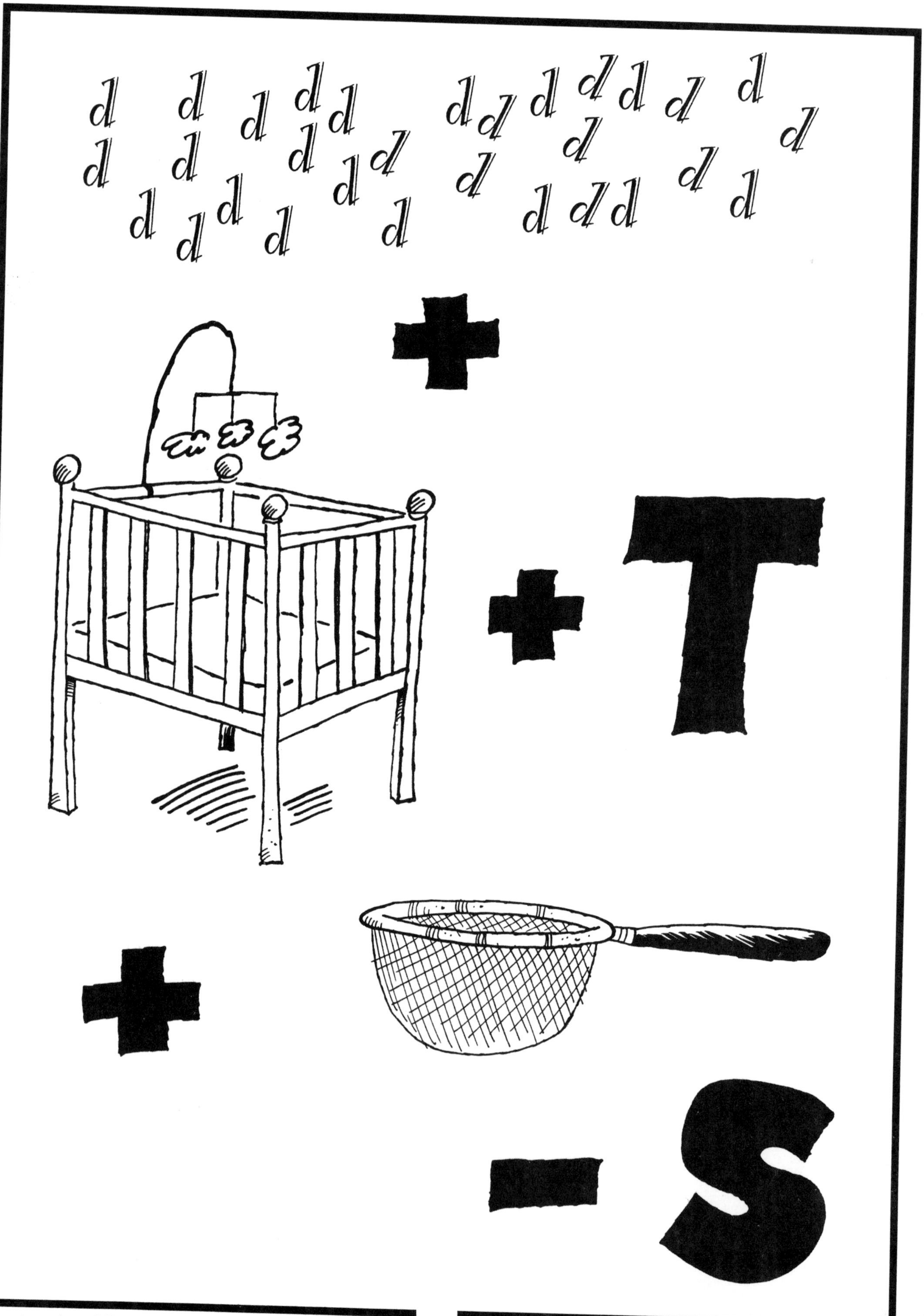

d d d d d d d d d d d d
d d d d d d d d d d
d d d d d d d d d d
d d d d d d d d d

+

+ **T**

+

− **S**

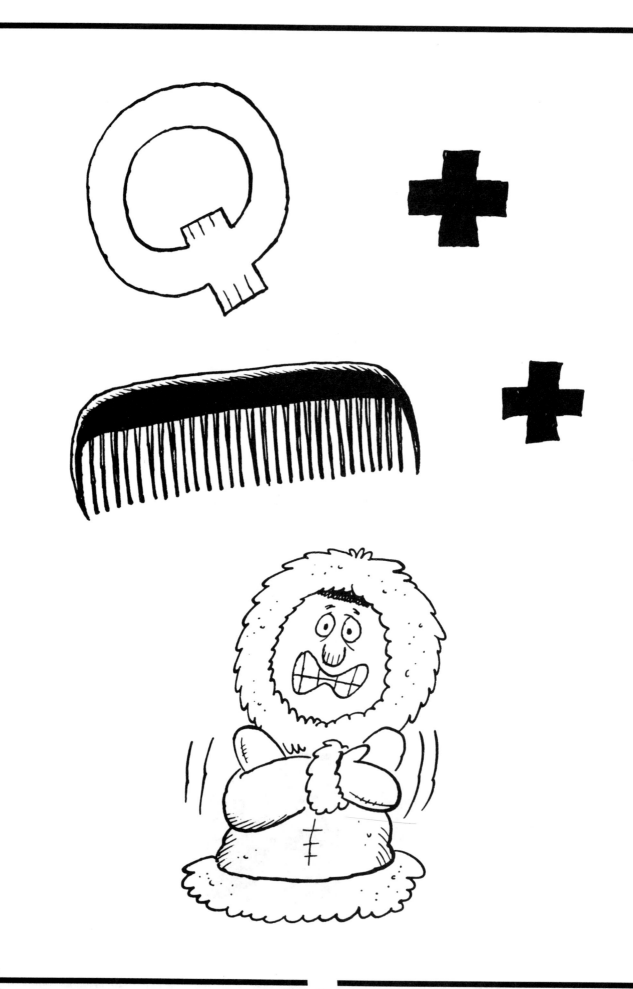

IF8363 Rebus Puzzle Activities

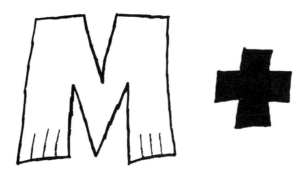

IF8363 Rebus Puzzle Activities

IF8363 Rebus Puzzle Activities

IF8363 Rebus Puzzle Activities

IF8363 Rebus Puzzle Activities

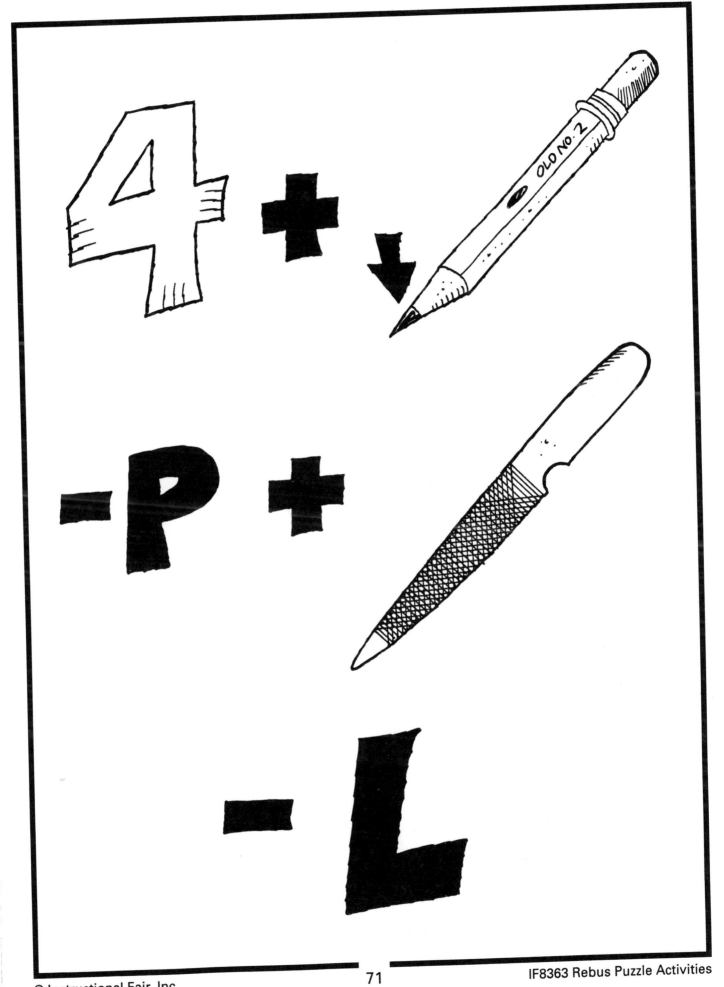

IF8363 Rebus Puzzle Activities

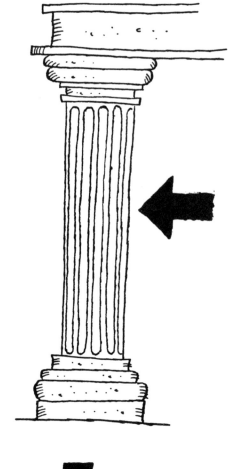

SCHOOL

IF8363 Rebus Puzzle Activities

IF8363 Rebus Puzzle Activities

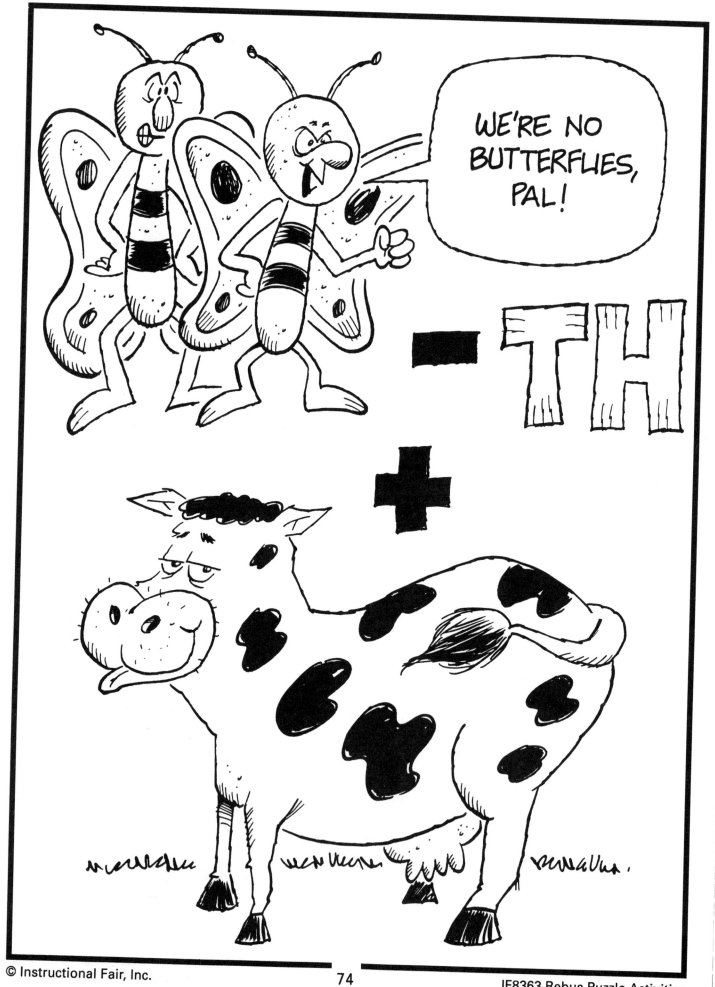

IF8363 Rebus Puzzle Activities

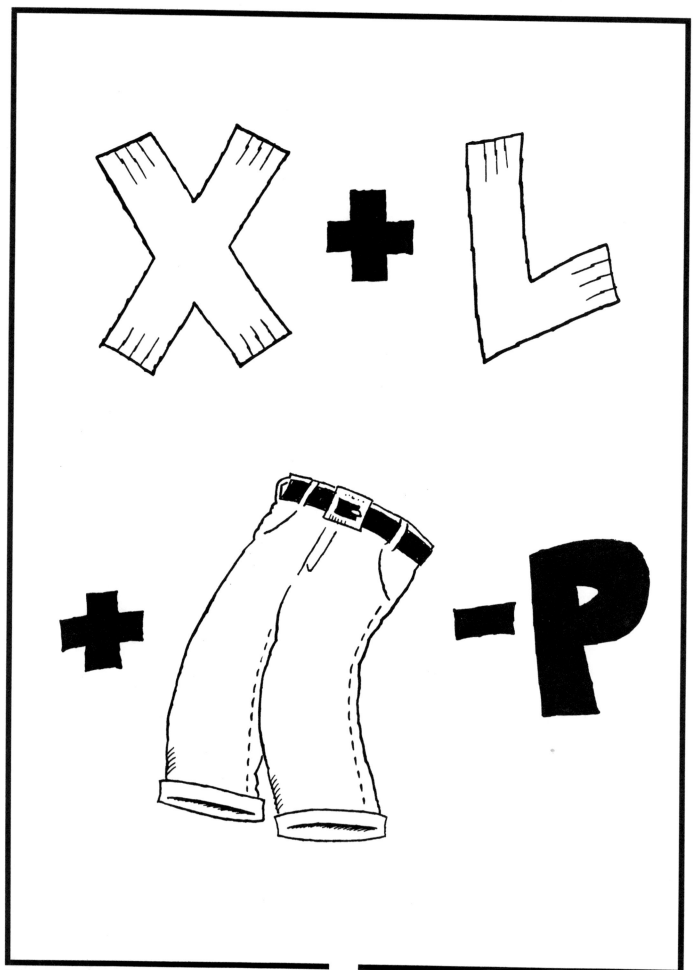

IF8363 Rebus Puzzle Activities

IF8363 Rebus Puzzle Activities

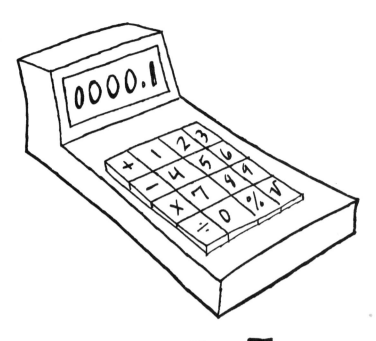

-CULATOR

+

+A

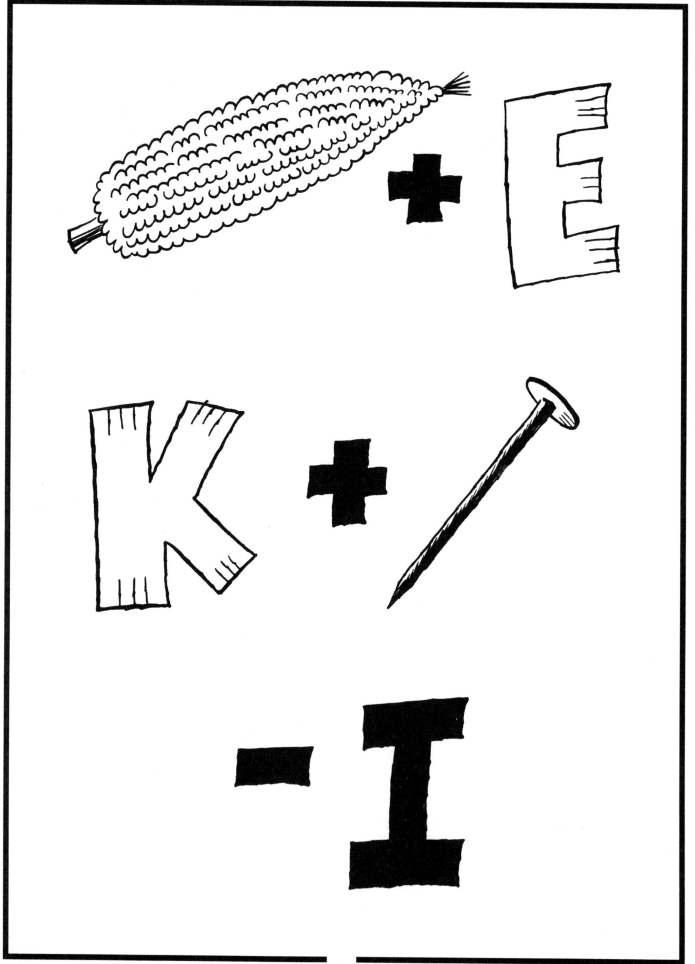

IF8363 Rebus Puzzle Activities

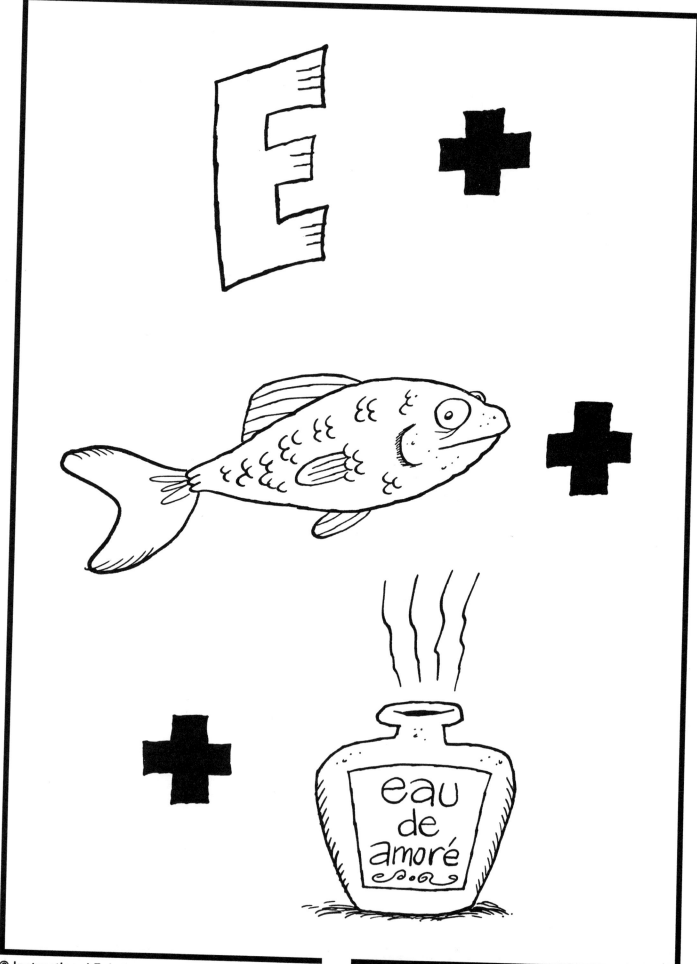

IF8363 Rebus Puzzle Activities

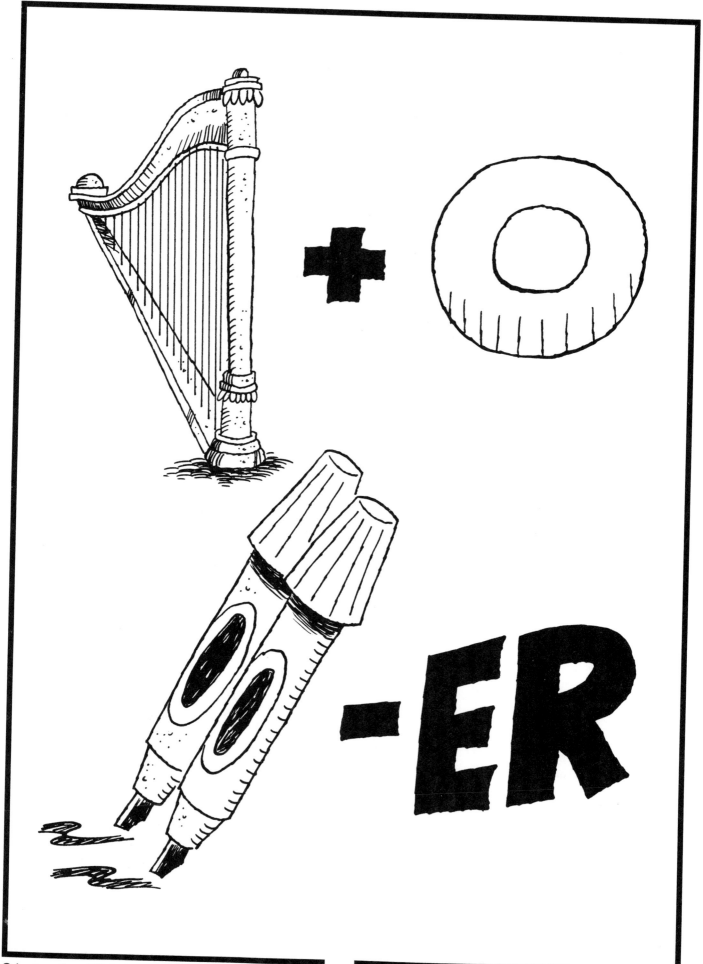

86

IF8363 Rebus Puzzle Activities

IF8363 Rebus Puzzle Activities

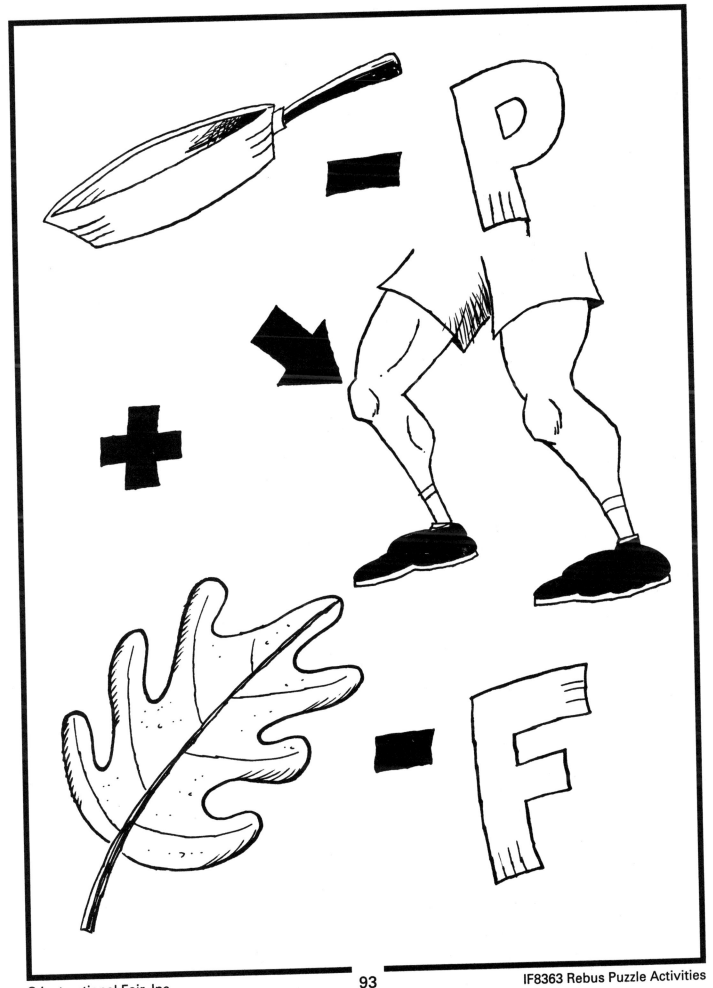

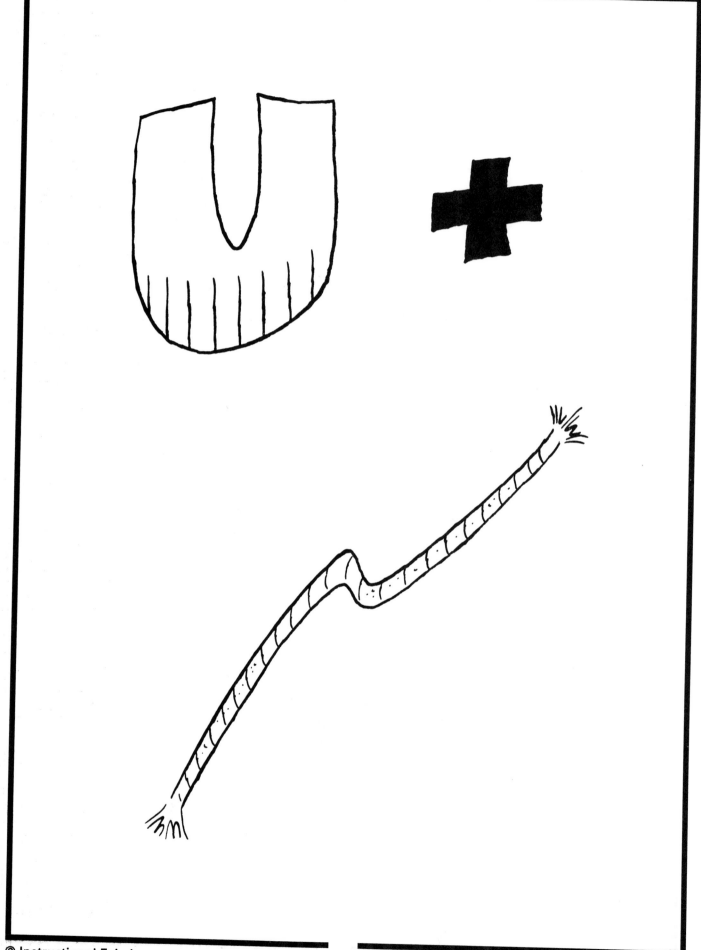

IF8363 Rebus Puzzle Activities

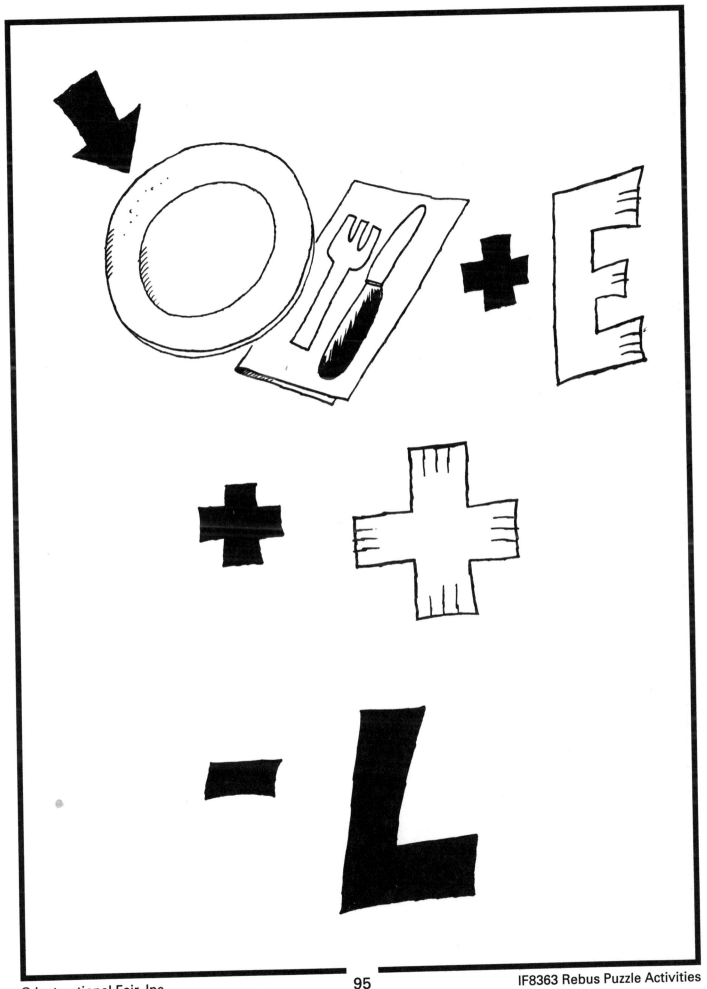

IF8363 Rebus Puzzle Activities

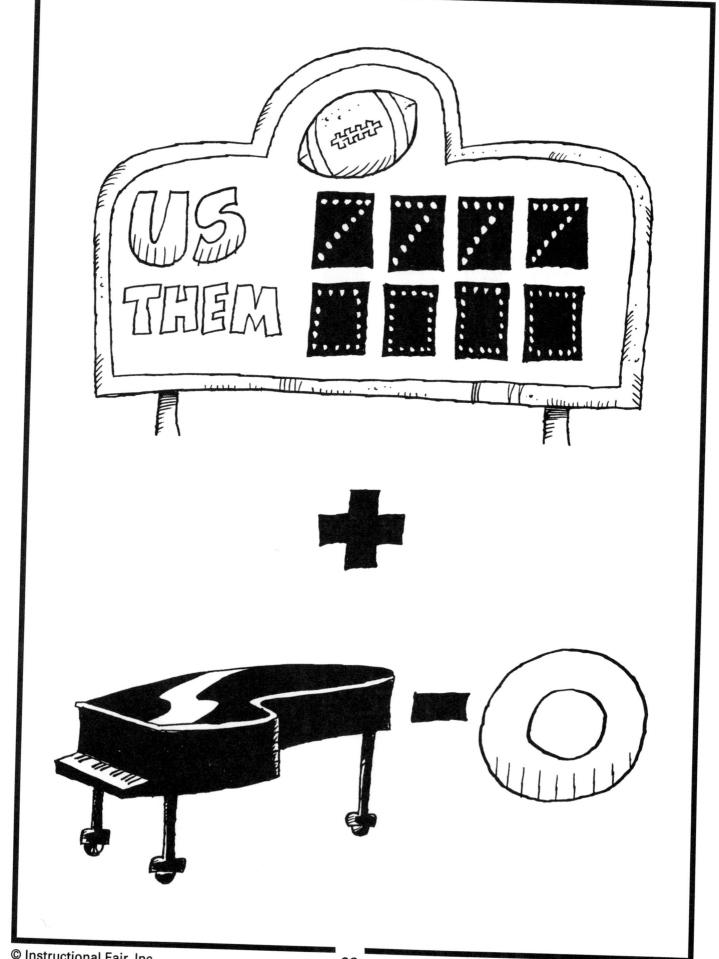

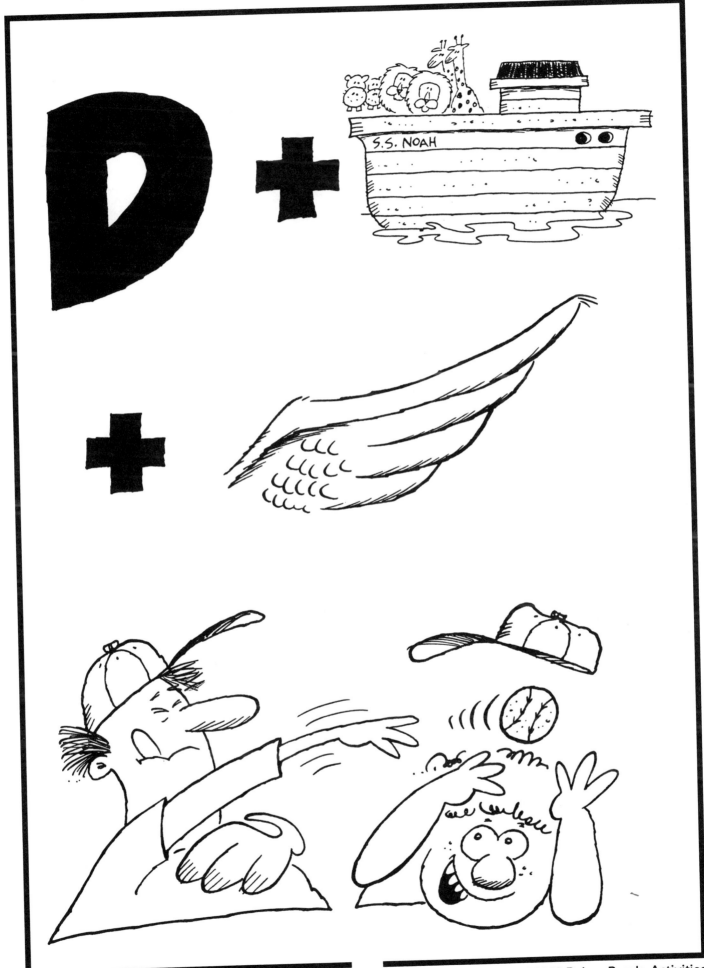

IF8363 Rebus Puzzle Activities

IF8363 Rebus Puzzle Activities

IF8363 Rebus Puzzle Activities

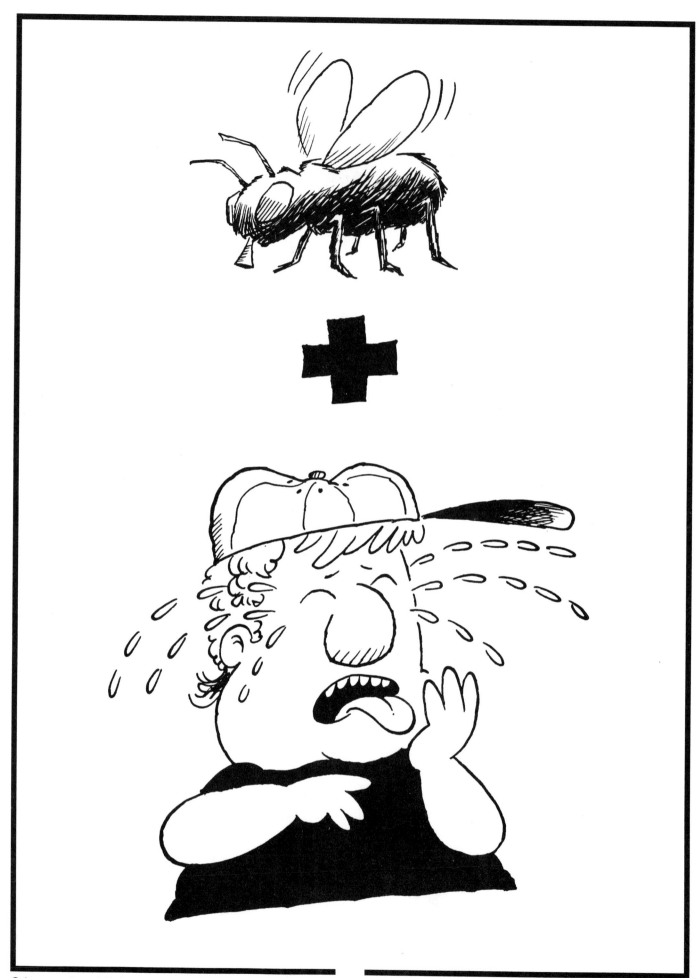

IF8363 Rebus Puzzle Activities

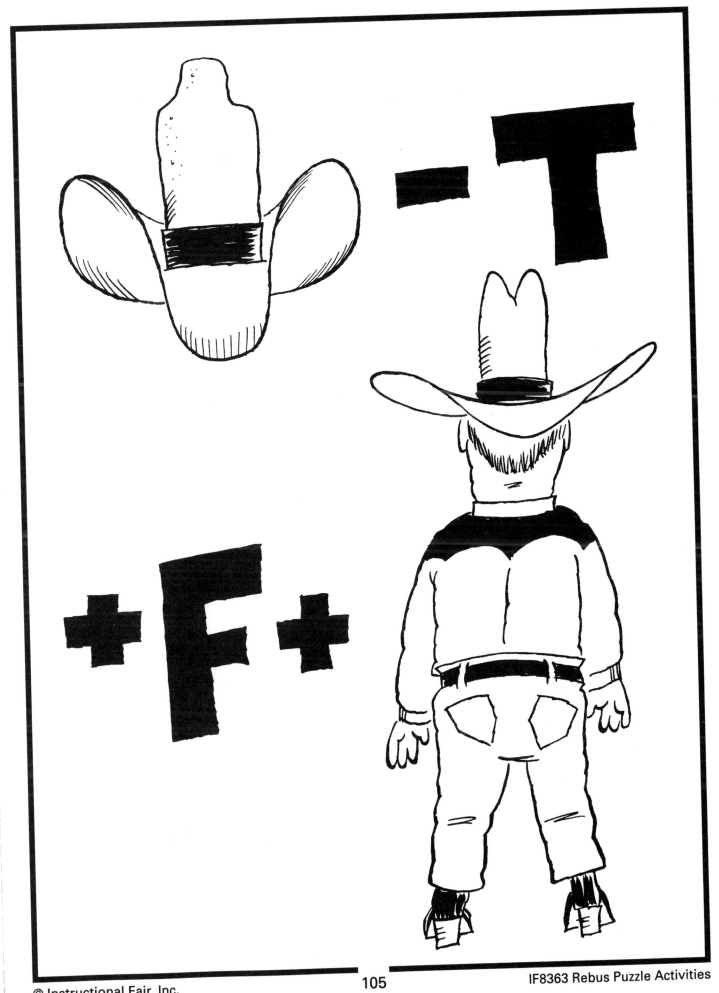

IF8363 Rebus Puzzle Activities

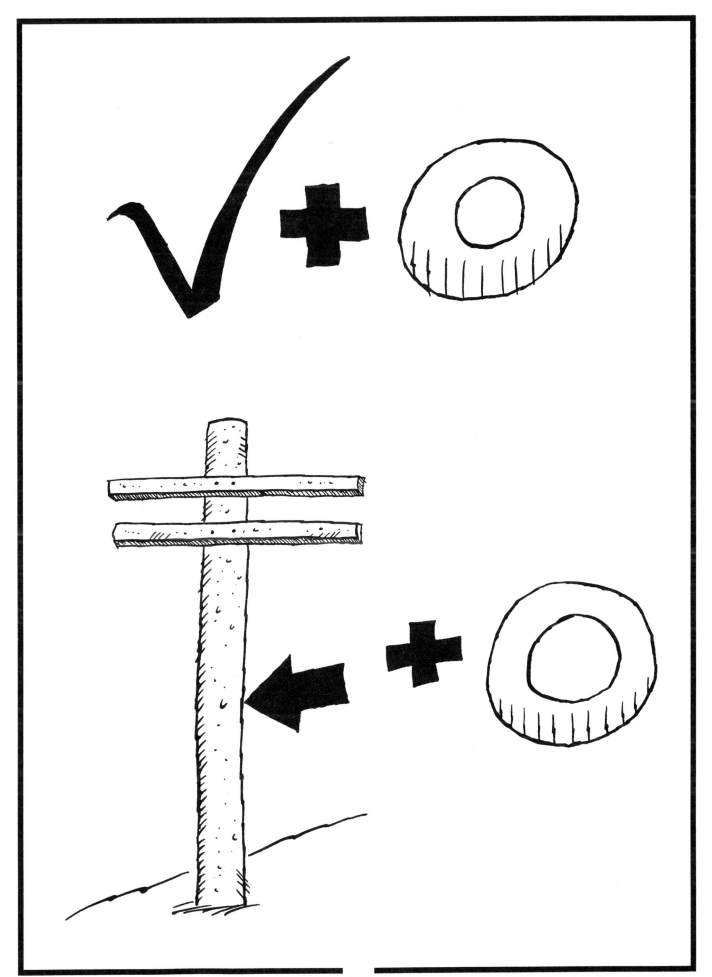

IF8363 Rebus Puzzle Activities

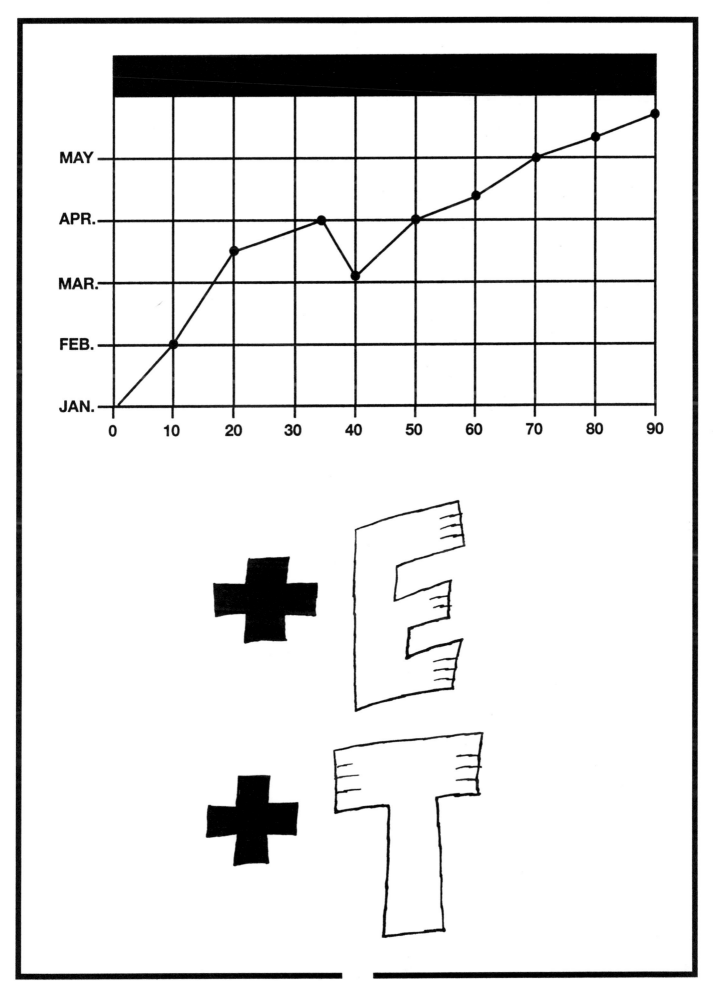

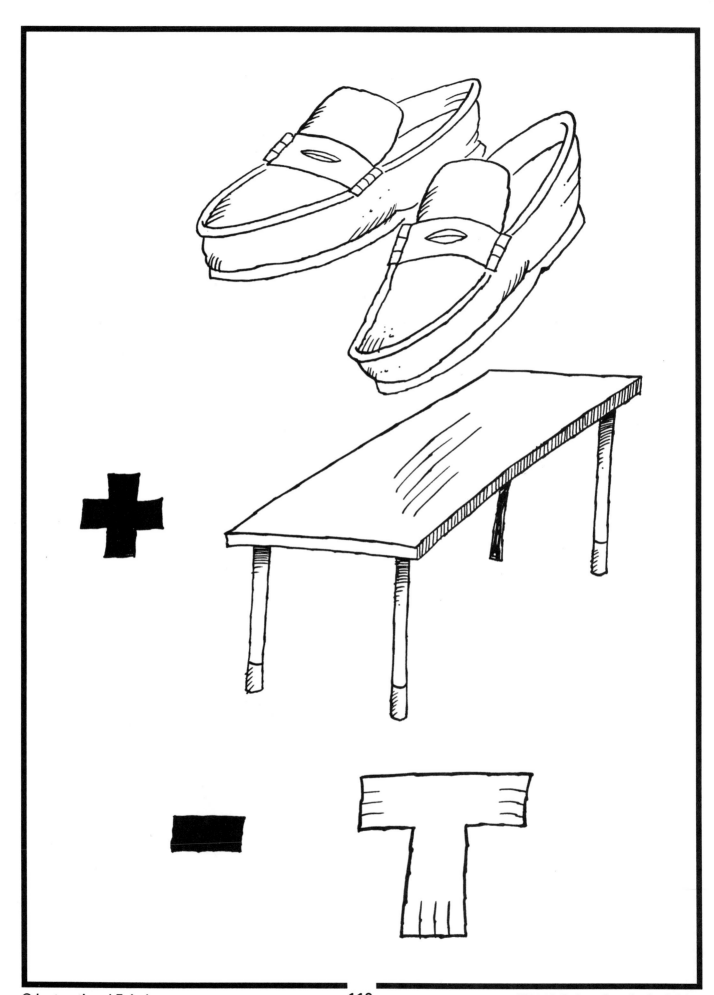

IF8363 Rebus Puzzle Activities

114

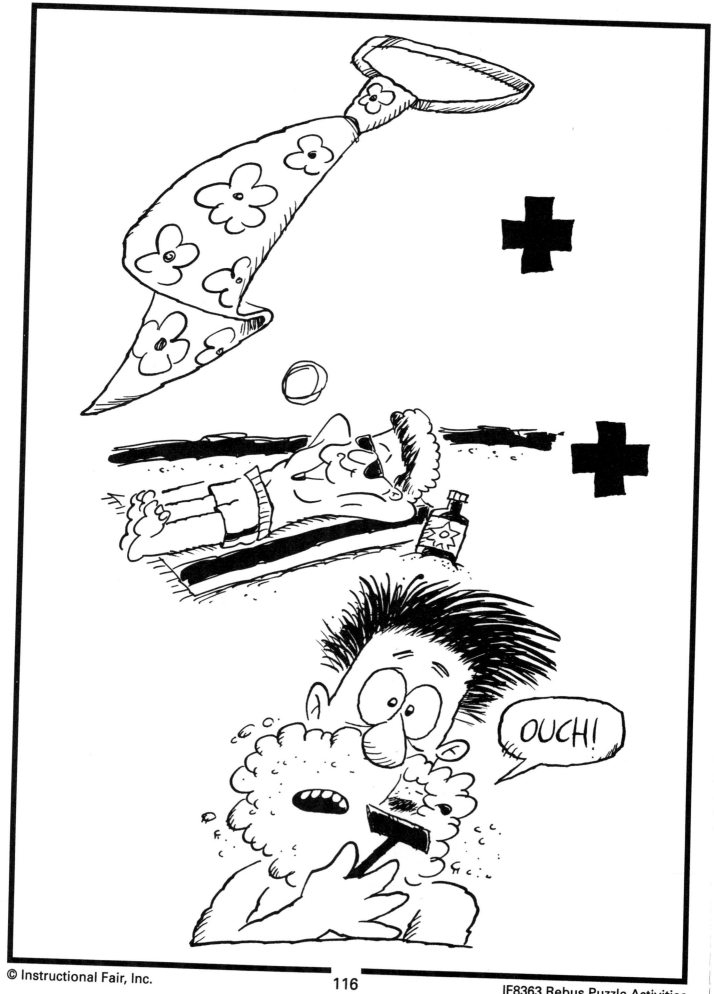

IF8363 Rebus Puzzle Activities

-SHOE

+ K +

It was a
dark and
stormy
night...

-D

IF8363 Rebus Puzzle Activities

IF8363 Rebus Puzzle Activities

IF8363 Rebus Puzzle Activities

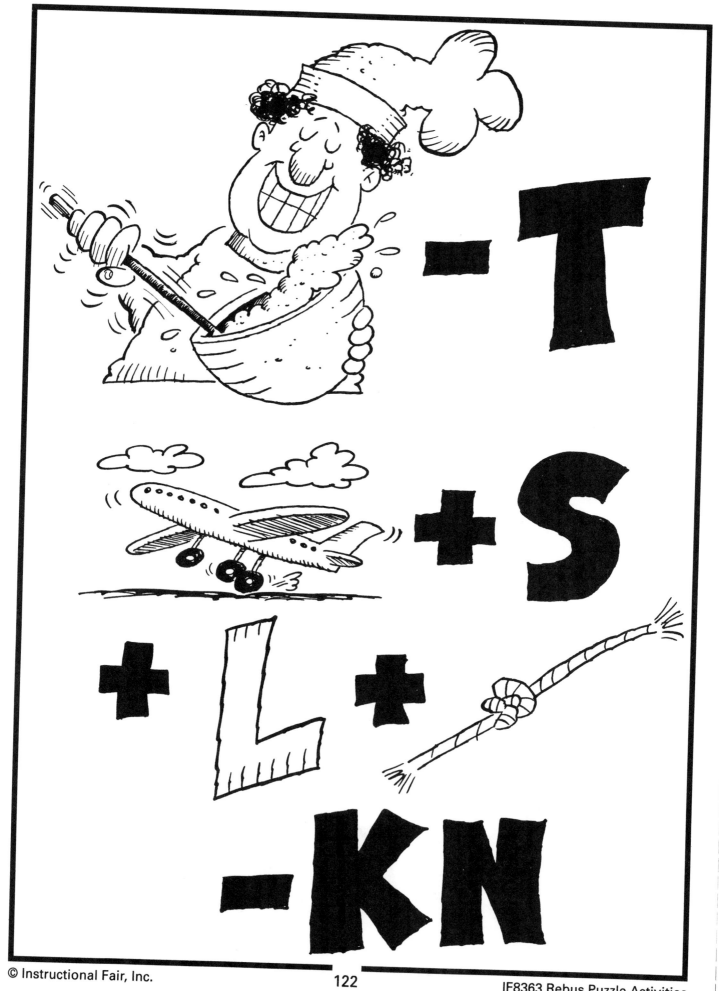

122

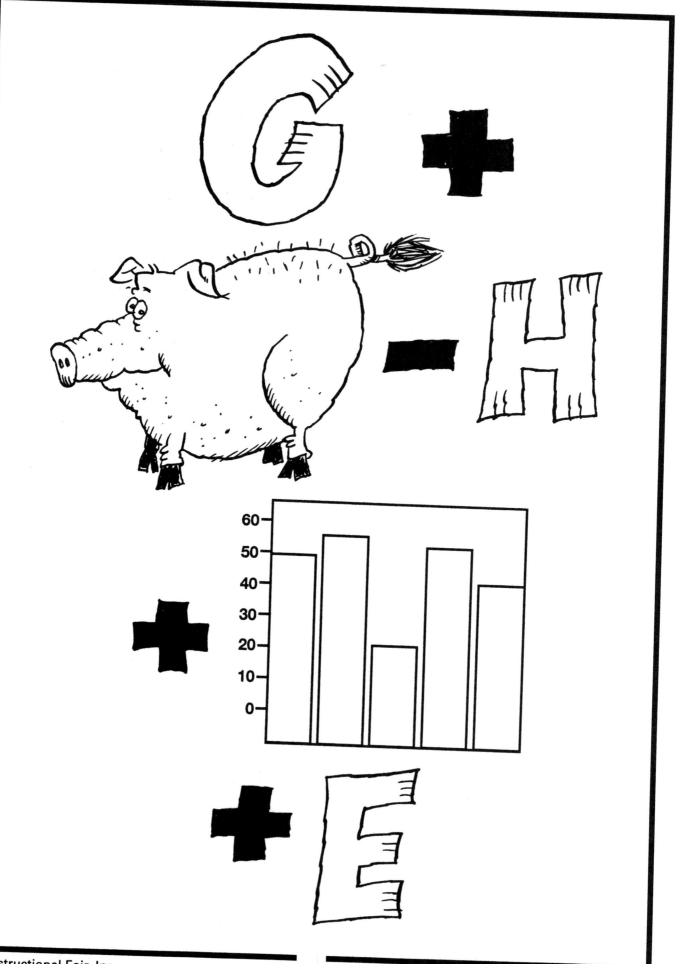

IF8363 Rebus Puzzle Activities

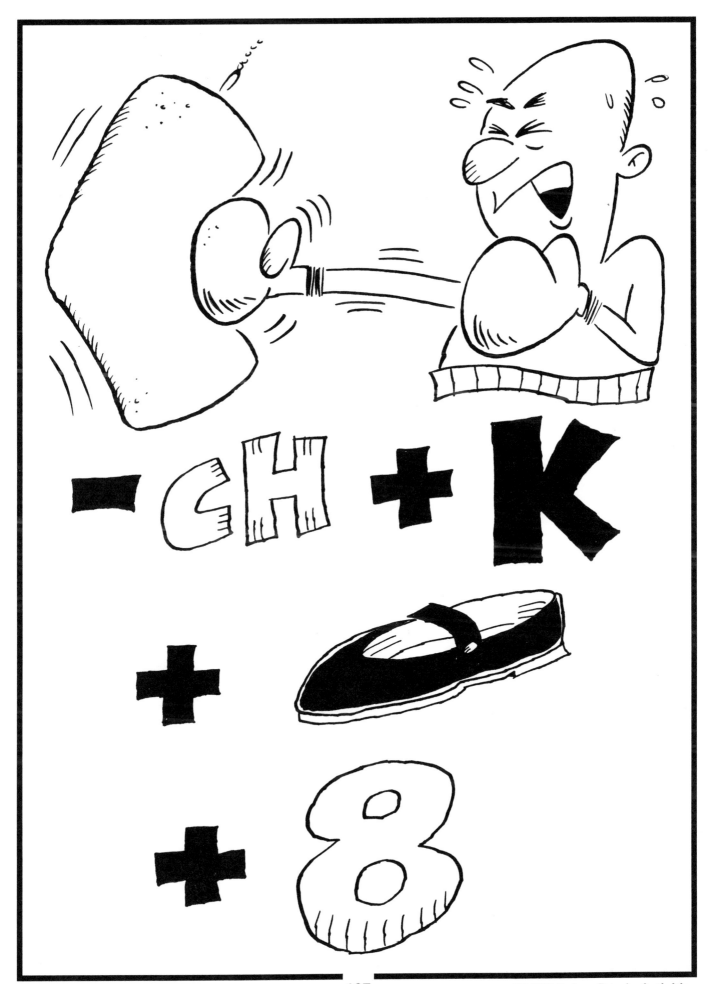

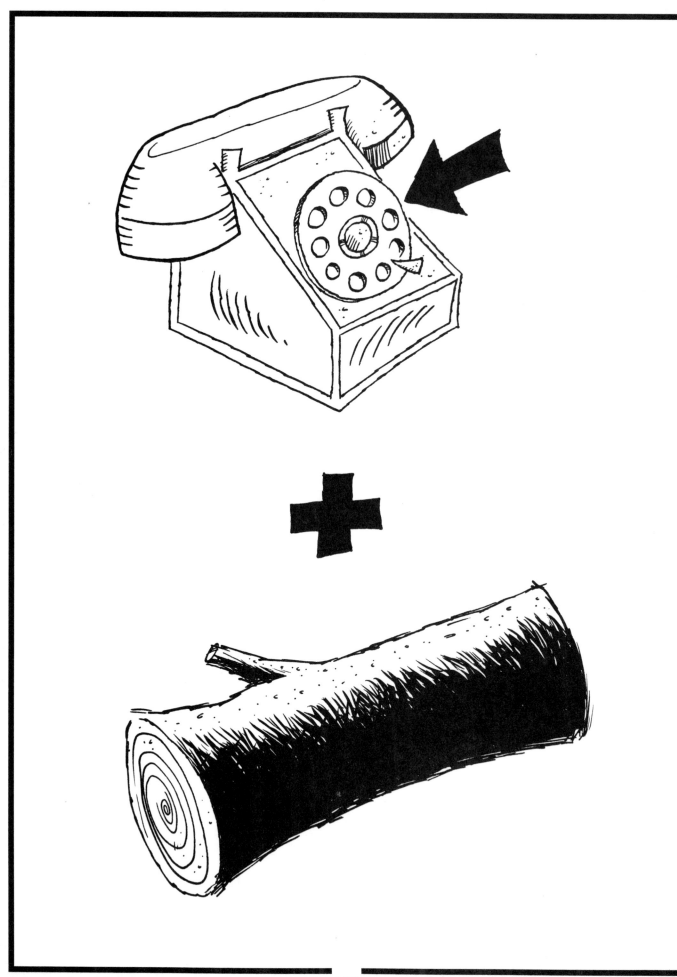

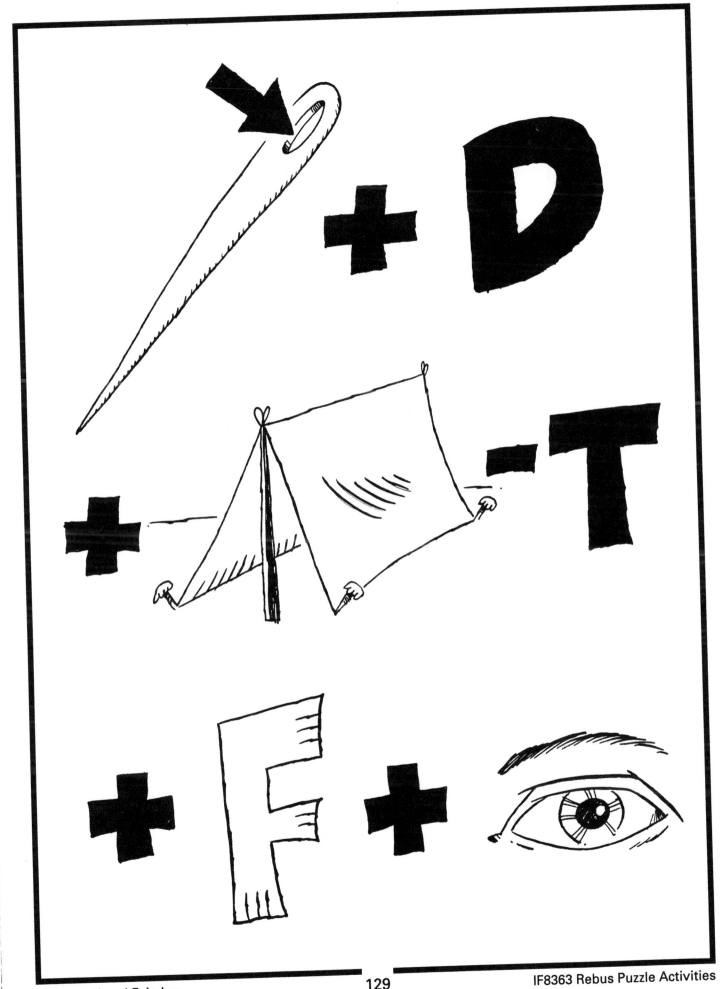

IF8363 Rebus Puzzle Activities

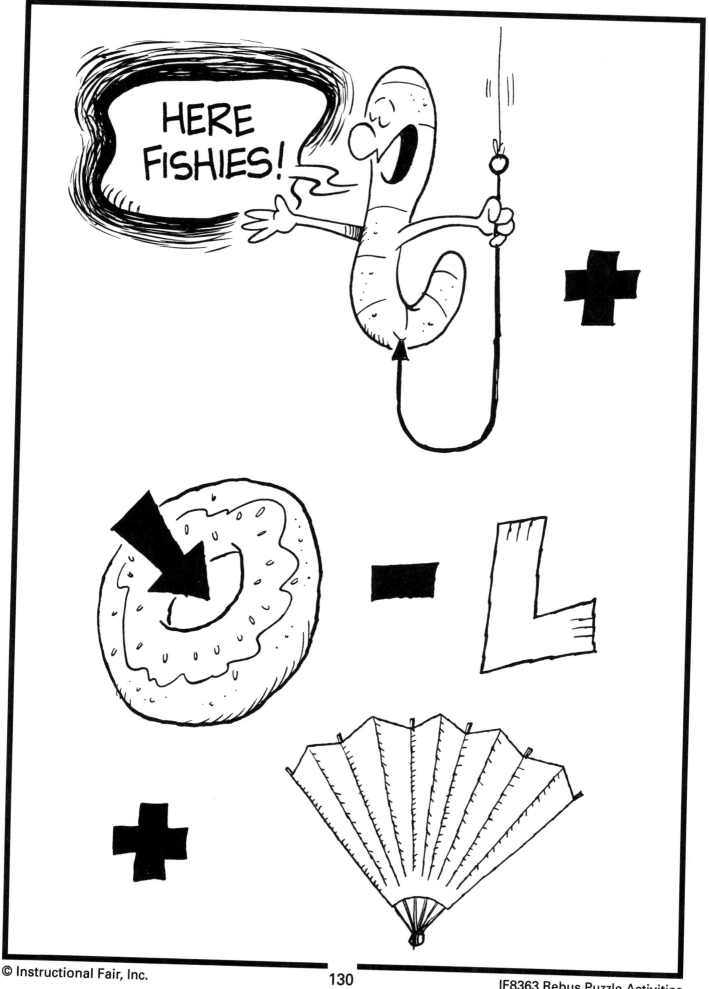

130

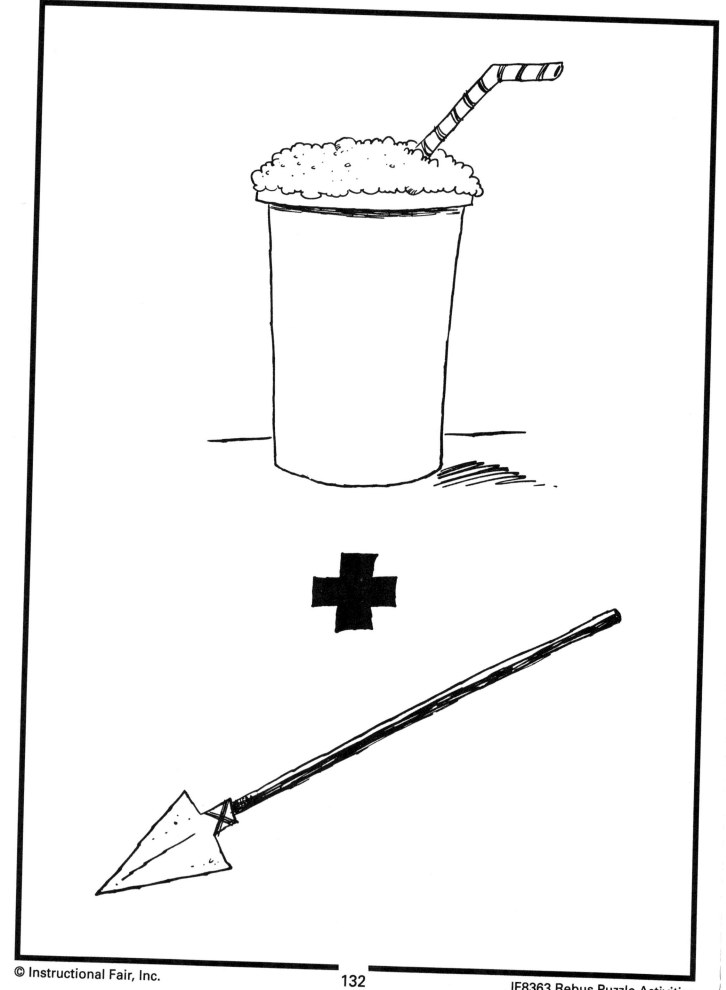

IF8363 Rebus Puzzle Activities

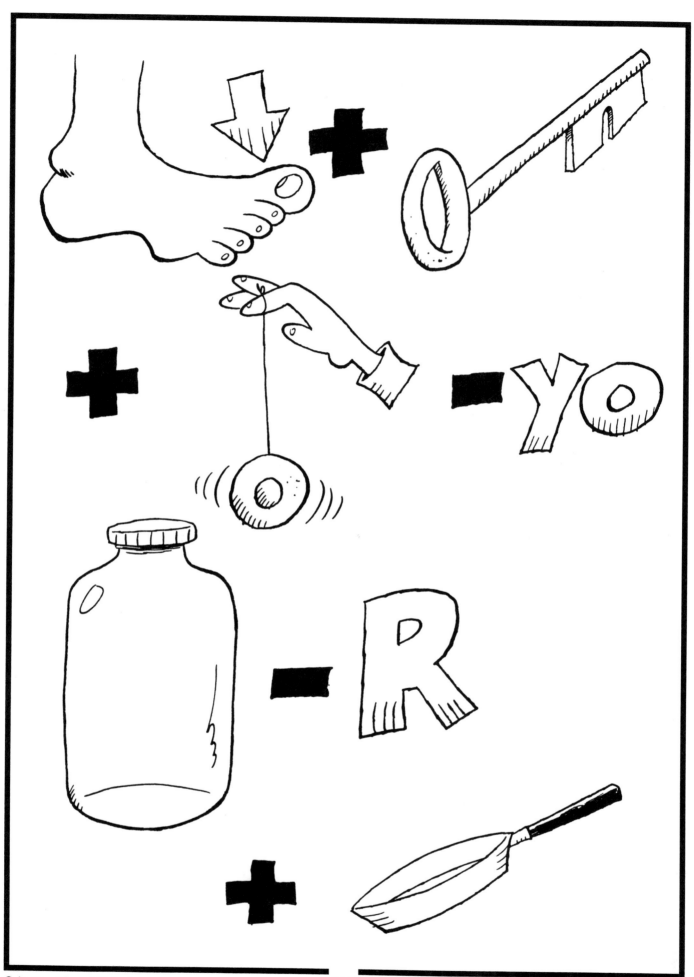

IF8363 Rebus Puzzle Activities

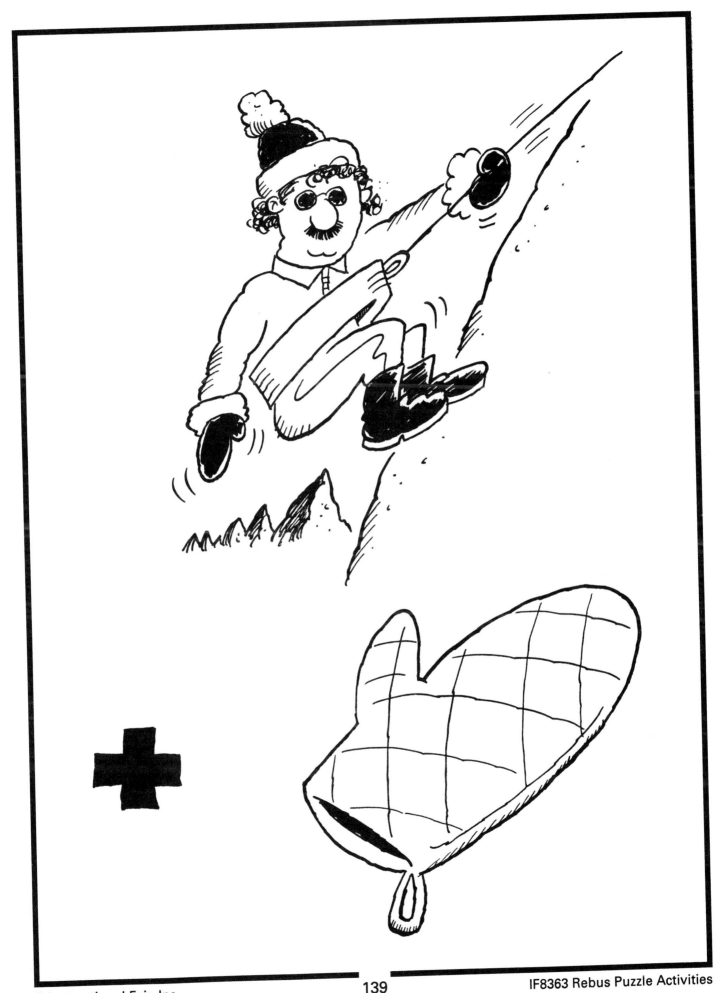

IF8363 Rebus Puzzle Activities

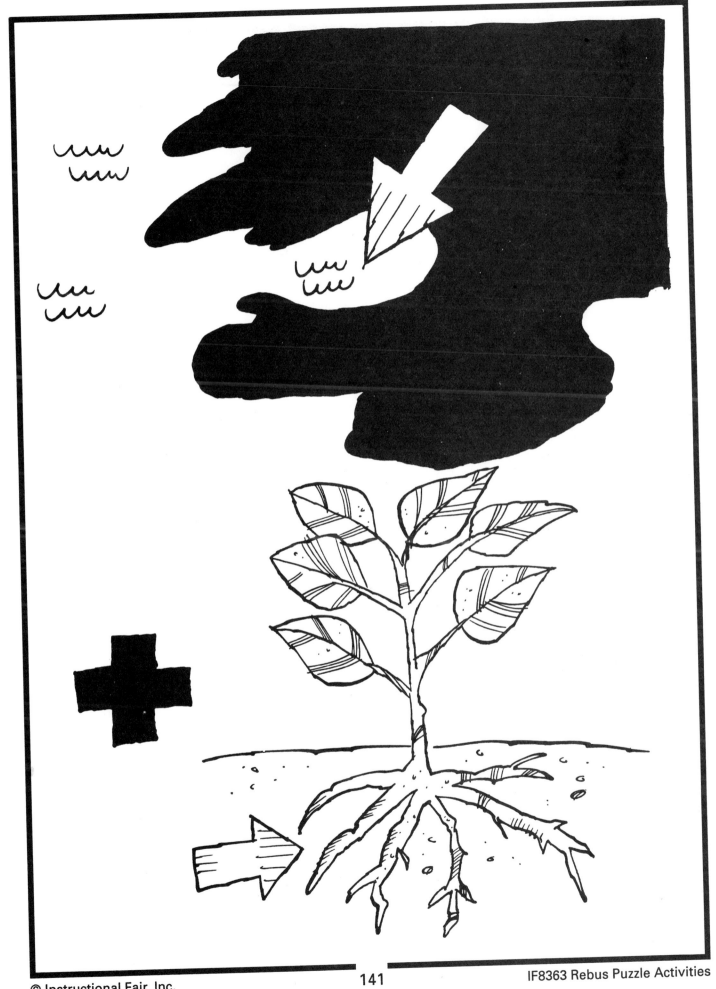

IF8363 Rebus Puzzle Activities

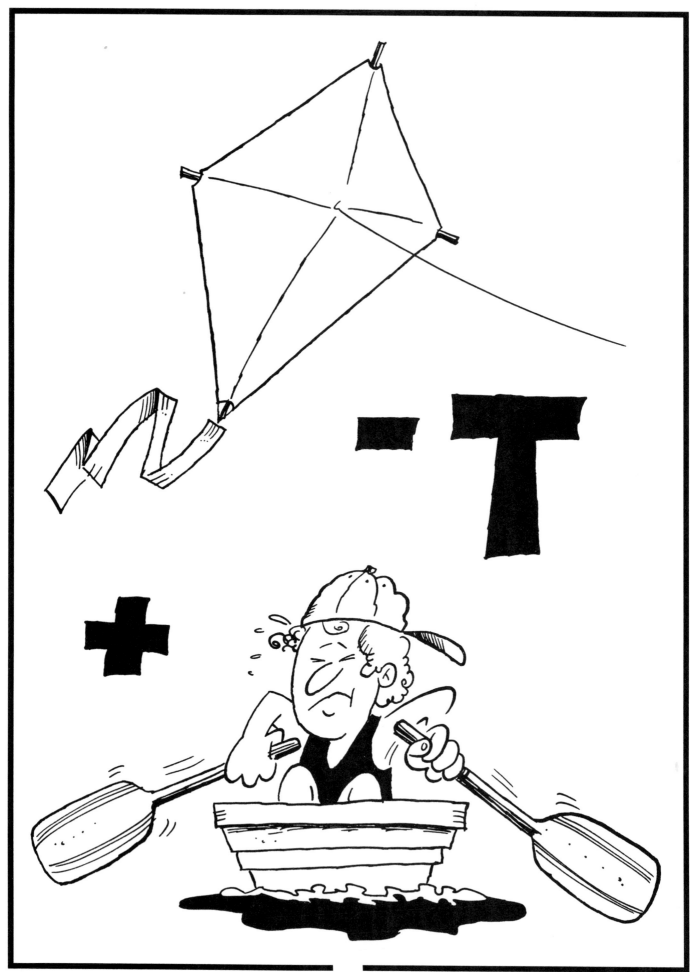

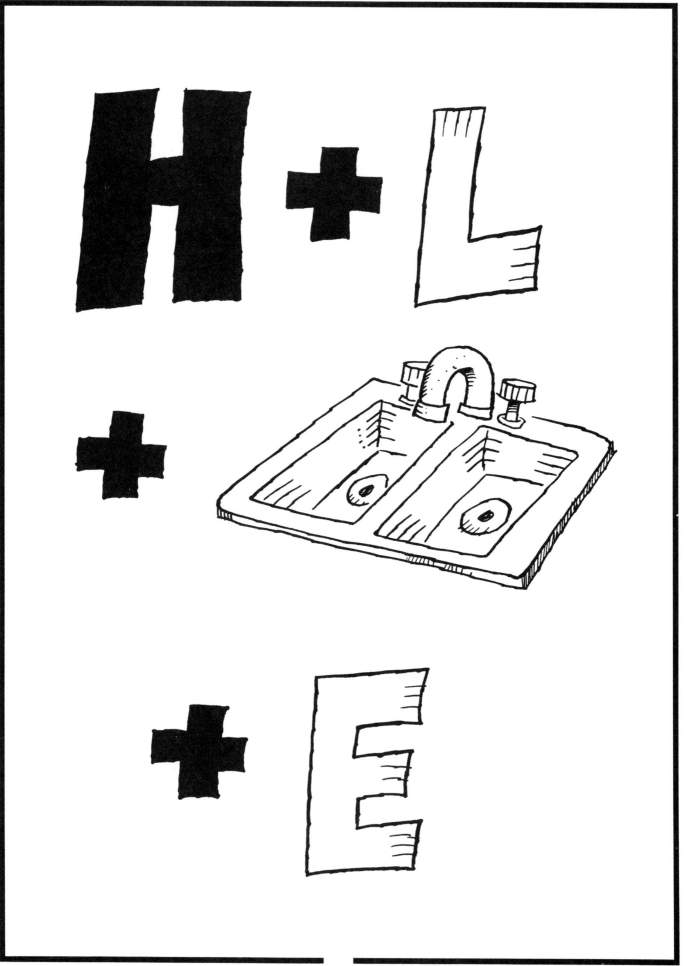

IF8363 Rebus Puzzle Activities

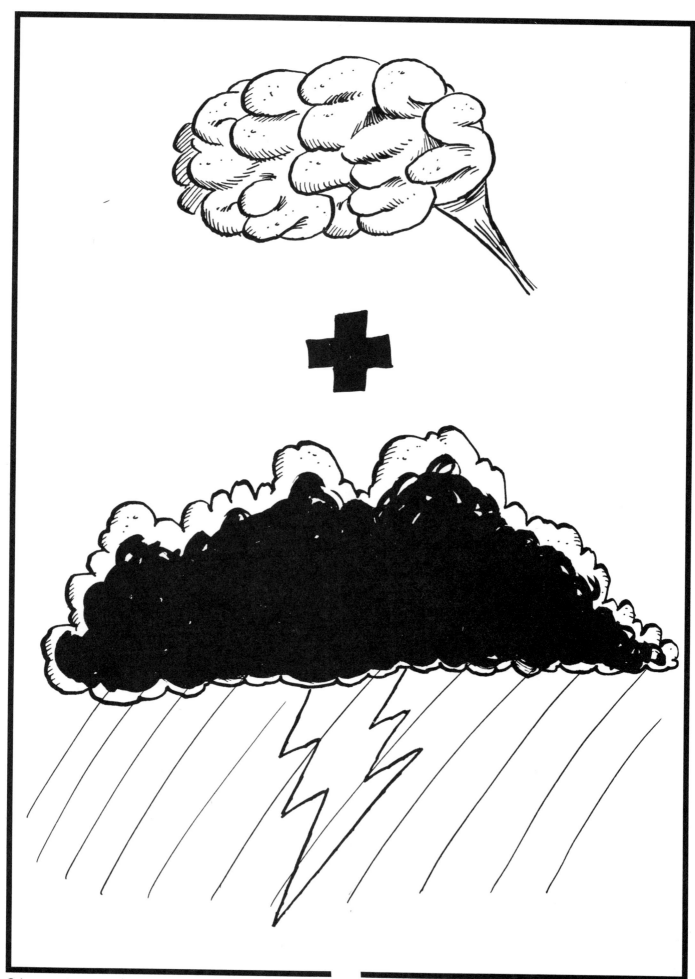

- cycle

+

149

IF8363 Rebus Puzzle Activities

IF8363 Rebus Puzzle Activities

IF8363 Rebus Puzzle Activities

IF8363 Rebus Puzzle Activities

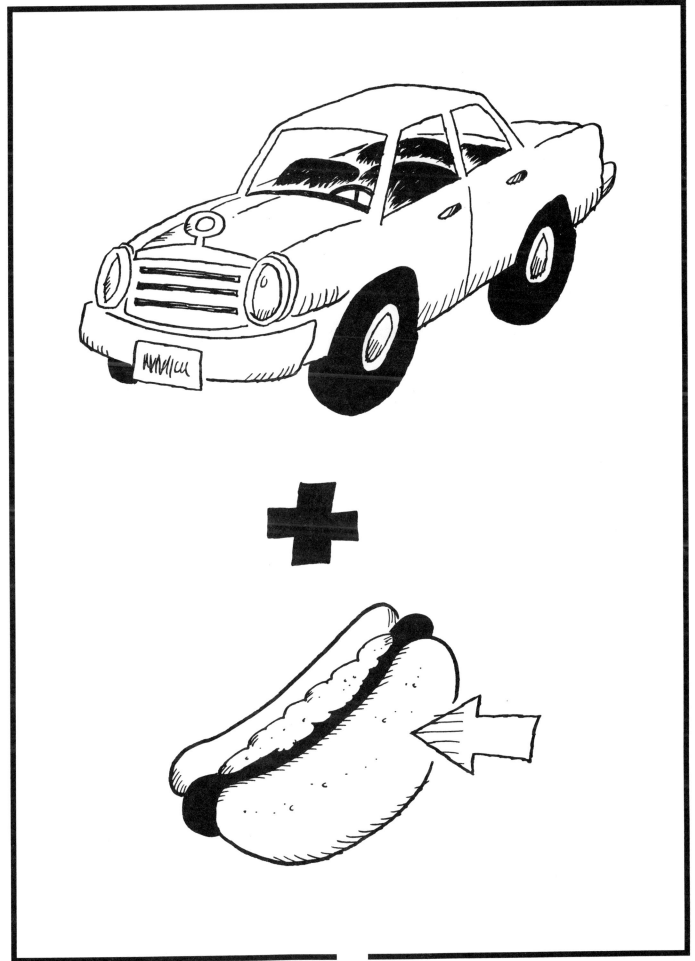

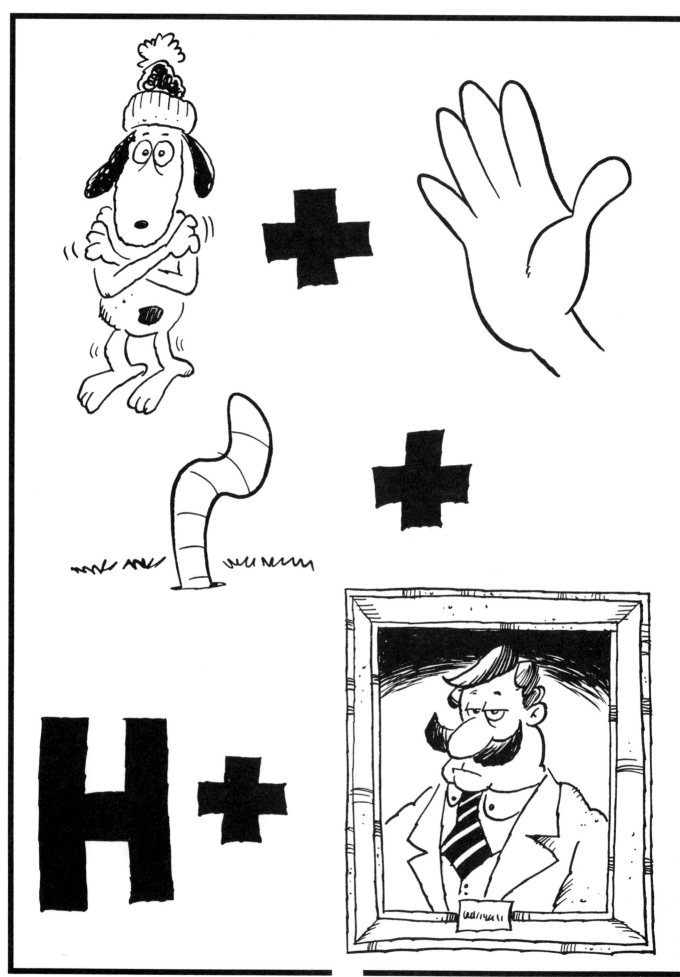

Answer Key